NATURE/SCIENCE ANNUAL

1975 NATURE/SCIENCE ANNUAL

EDITION

TIME-LIFE BOOKS, NEW YORK

TIME-LIFE BOOKS

FOUNDER: Henry R. Luce 1898-1967

Editor-in-Chief: Hedley Donovan
Chairman of the Board: Andrew Heiskell
President: James R. Shepley
Group Vice President: Rhett Austell
Vice Chairman: Roy E. Larsen

MANAGING EDITOR: Jerry Korn
Assistant Managing Editors: Ezra Bowen,
David Maness, Martin Mann, A. B. C. Whipple
Planning Director: Oliver E. Allen
Art Director: Sheldon Cotler
Chief of Research: Beatrice T. Dobie
Director of Photography: Melvin L. Scott
Senior Text Editor: Diana Hirsh
Assistant Art Director: Arnold C. Holeywell
Assistant Chief of Research: Myra Mangan

PUBLISHER: Joan D. Manley
General Manager: John D. McSweeney
Business Manager: Nicholas J. C. Ingleton
Sales Director: Carl G. Jaeger
Promotion Director: Paul R. Stewart
Public Relations Director: Nicholas Benton

NATURE/SCIENCE ANNUAL

EDITOR: Jane D. Alexander
Staff Writer: James A. Randall
Designer: Lee Stausland
Chief Researchers: Catherine Ireys, Ann Morrison
Researchers: Starr Badger, Jessy Faubert,
Tonna Gibert, Celeste Madden, Millie Swanson,
Gretchen Wessels
Editorial Assistant: Karen Z. Barnard

EDITORIAL PRODUCTION
Production Editor: Douglas B. Graham
Assistant Production Editors: Gennaro C. Esposito,
Feliciano Madrid
Quality Director: Robert L. Young
Assistant Quality Director: James J. Cox
Copy Staff: Rosalind Stubenberg (chief),
Mary Ellen Slate, Charles Blackwell,
Barbara Quarmby, Florence Keith, Pearl Sverdlin
Picture Department: Dolores A. Littles,
Carolyn Turman
Traffic: Carmen McLellan

ON THE COVER

Using the suction cups on the tips of its three-digited forefeet, a Cuban tree frog grasps the leaf of a philodendron in suburban Miami. One of many new species that have come into Florida, the frog is a nuisance despite its human-like smile—it climbs into electrical relay boxes, shorts out circuits and causes blackouts.

Valuable assistance in preparing this book was provided by the following departments and individuals of Time Inc.: Editorial Production, Norman Airey; Library, Benjamin Lightman; Picture Collection, Doris O'Neil; Photographic Laboratory, George Karas; TIME-LIFE News Service, Murray J. Gart; Correspondents Maria Vincenza Aloisi and Josephine du Brusle (Paris), Margot Hapgood and Dorothy Bacon (London), Elisabeth Kraemer (Bonn), Ann Natanson (Rome), S. Chang (Tokyo), Dag Christensen (Oslo), John Dunn (Melbourne), Elizabeth Hawley (Kathmandu), Sandra Hinson (Orlando), Mary Johnson (Stockholm), Anton Koene and Sue Masterman (Rijswijk, Netherlands), Robert L. Kroon (Geneva), Lucky Marmon (Jerusalem), Knud Meister (Copenhagen), Jane Reicker (Miami), James Shepherd (New Delhi), Pat Tucker (Washington), Bing Wong (Hong Kong).

Contents

formation on the sun than the sum of man's previous investigations since the time of Galileo. One scientist exclaimed, with excusable hyperbole: "We have more data than anybody has collected on anything!"

The data from the Skylab mission is indeed mountainous—more than 300,000 pictures that if stacked would be as tall as the Washington Monument. Yet even this mass of information will probably not dispel the solar mysteries that have puzzled astronomers for ages.

Many of the photographs are other-worldly, their dramatic impact heightened by false colors introduced with computers so that scientists can study features invisible to the human eye. Among the pictures are an almost full view of the sun's tenuous outer atmosphere, or corona, a giant fiery mass hurtling from the sun's surface at a million miles an hour, and the never-before-seen triggering of one solar flare by another.

To obtain these pictures, three teams of astronauts probed the sun from May of 1973 to February 1974—spending a total of 171 days in space. Their instrument was a $50-million battery of eight instruments making up the Apollo Telescope Mount (ATM), which took pictures not only in visible light but in many other kinds of solar radiation—X-rays, ultraviolet rays—normally blocked from view by the atmosphere. ATM's very first X-ray photograph *(opposite)* shattered a central tenet of solar theory. Astronomers thought the corona was a steady blanket of hot gas—a quiet stage on which an occasional violent act was played out. But this "quiet corona" is simply not there. The X-ray photographs reveal neither uniformity nor stability, but a realm of constant contrast and change.

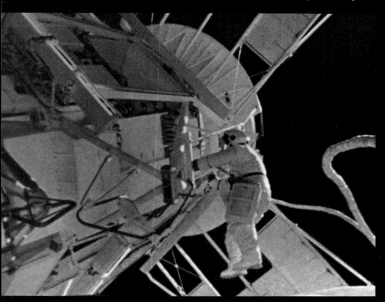

Suspended against the black void of space and secured by his life-sustaining oxygen line, Astronaut Pete Conrad retrieves film from one of eight solar telescopes in Skylab.

A color-coded X-ray portrait of the sun's corona reveals unexpected contrasts: hot active regions (yellow), cool dark "holes," and mysterious, short-lived bright points.

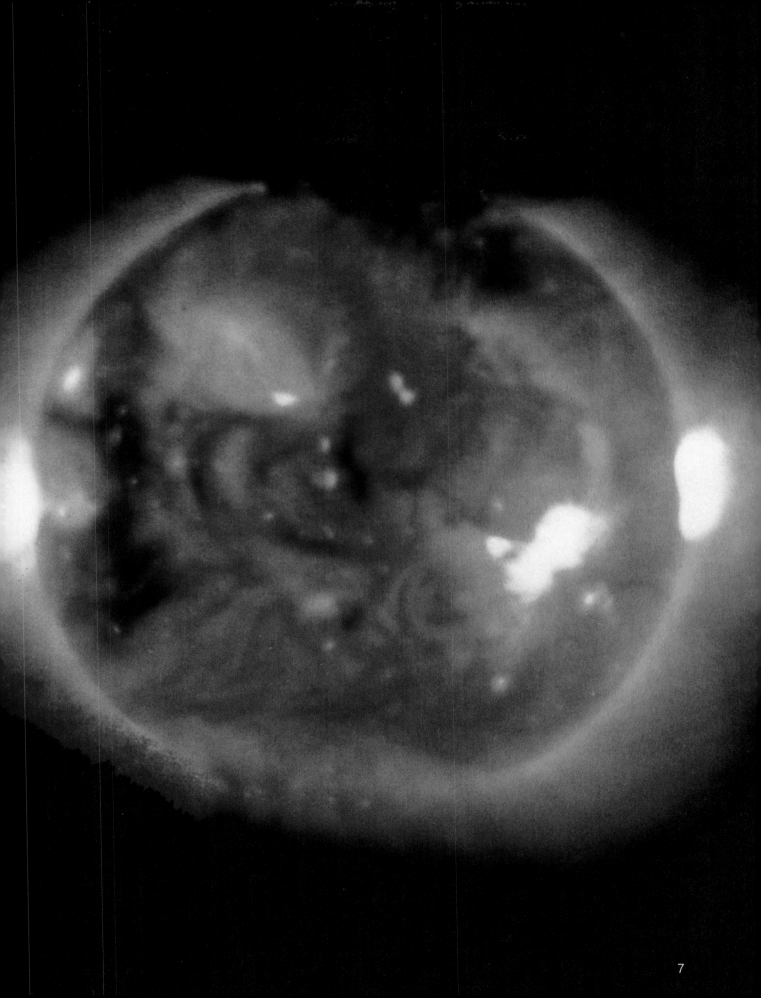

A Giant Bubble of Fiery Gas

Because the sun's surface is so dazzling to the human eye, the thin outer atmosphere, or corona, cannot be seen under ordinary conditions. In fact, earthbound astronomers can view this veil of gases only when the moon obscures the solar disc during a total eclipse, or when an eclipse is simulated with a coronagraph, a telescope fitted with a metal "moon" to block the disc. Even then the earth's atmosphere prevents clear observation of the corona, blurring its faint light.

However, Skylab was clear of earth's atmospheric screen, and its coronagraph took clear views—including one of an astounding phenomenon. About every 48 hours, Skylab recorded massive ejections of solar material, some as big across as the sun itself, which moved through the corona at tremendous speeds. These coronal "transients," carrying electrically charged particles that create powerful magnetic forces, may account for previously unexplained magnetic disturbances detected near earth.

In this natural solar eclipse, the moon covers the sun's disc, allowing the dim corona to be seen.

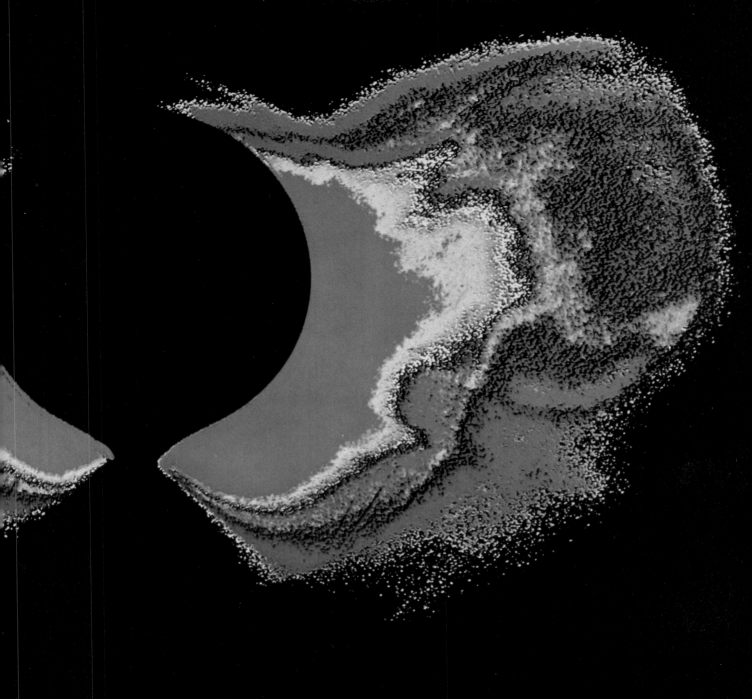

This huge bubble of gas blasting through the corona at almost a million miles an hour was recorded by Skylab's coronagraph, which simulates a natural eclipse by mechanically blocking the sun's disc. The colors show degrees of brightness; the red near the disc is the brightest area while the outermost yellow fringe is the dimmest.

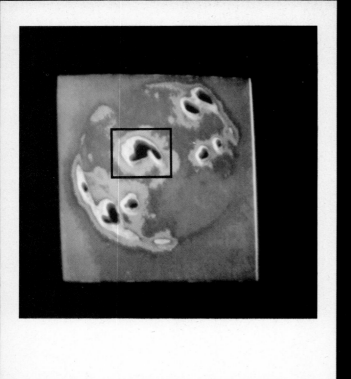

Scientists saw a peculiar two-part flare development (dark blue area inside rectangle) in this artificially colored image of the sun made from a Skylab telescope photograp which was taken about eight hours after flare activity commenced. Other blue spots on the solar disc—the blue indicates high temperature—are potential flare regions.

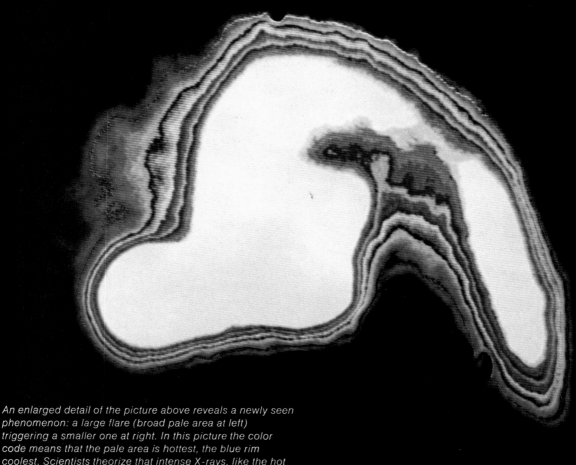

An enlarged detail of the picture above reveals a newly seen phenomenon: a large flare (broad pale area at left) triggering a smaller one at right. In this picture the color code means that the pale area is hottest, the blue rim coolest. Scientists theorize that intense X-rays, like the hot

Mysterious Birth of a Solar Flare

The huge bursts of radiation from the sun called solar flares are the bogeymen of space. They have been accused of causing everything from stock market dips to warts. What is certain is that flares do affect human affairs—they interfere with radio communications and electronic instruments, and they might cause injury to passengers aboard proposed extreme-high-altitude airliners. Therefore, forecasting flares has assumed great practical importance. Knowing how flares are triggered would be a great aid to accurate prediction, but gathering the facts has been difficult because flares emit much of their light as X-rays, which are blocked by the earth's atmosphere. But Skylab, flying above this region, was able to observe the building of a flare unhindered.

Looking at a print of a Skylab photograph, scientists spotted an intriguing pattern of X-ray emissions *(opposite, top)*. Then, when a computer was used to build a more detailed picture, color-coding it to indicate variations in temperature and X-ray intensity, a unique feature was revealed: a large flare apparently triggering a smaller flare *(below, left)*. Because Skylab's cameras had been snapping continuously, scientists could look at earlier pictures and find a view of the same area of the sun as it was three hours before the start of the flare activity. They were able to pinpoint the flare's beginning *(below)* and trace its development—a start toward the goal of charting flares with the precision of weather forecasters watching the buildup of a hurricane.

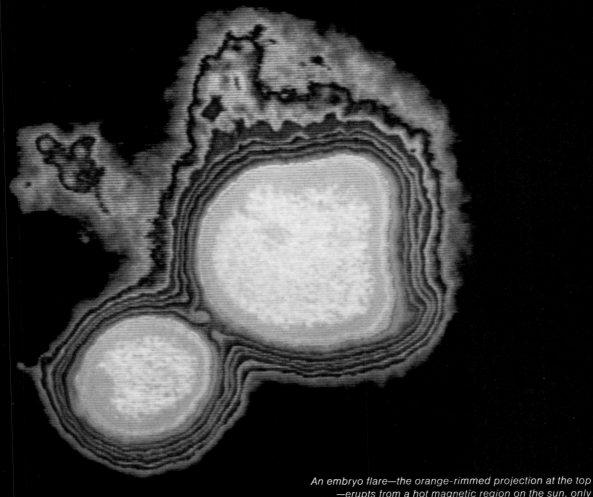

An embryo flare—the orange-rimmed projection at the top —erupts from a hot magnetic region on the sun, only to die shortly after this Skylab picture was photographed. A smaller proto-flare—the projection to the upper left—is actually the beginning of the big flare on the opposite page.

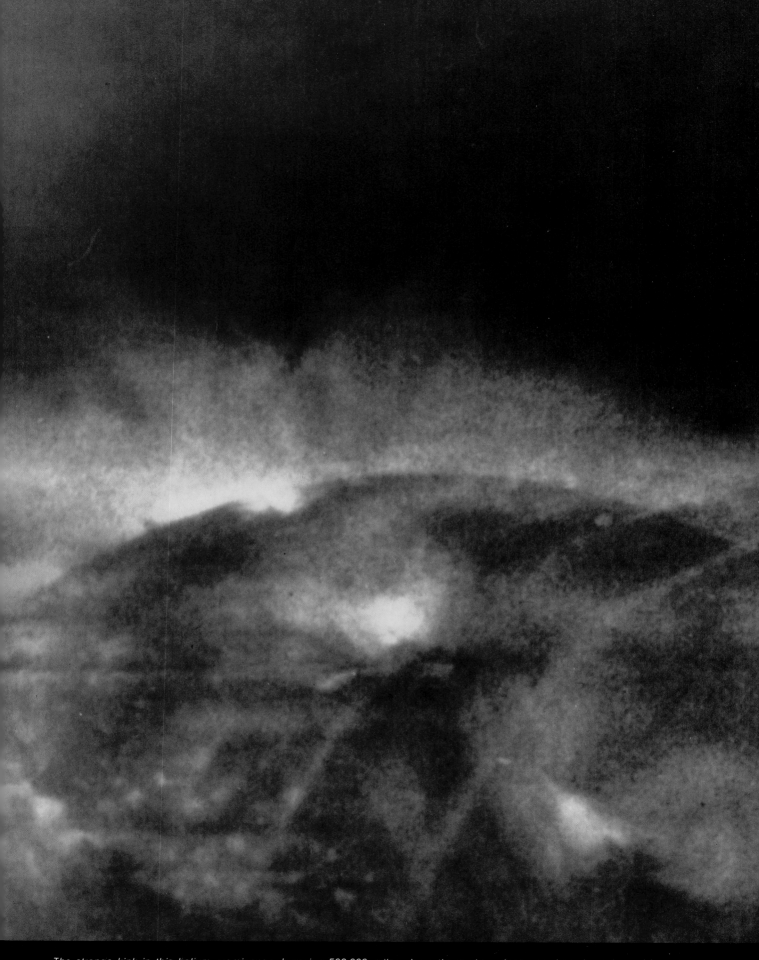

The strange kink in this helium prominence, hovering 500,000 miles above the sun's surface, may have been formed by solar matter

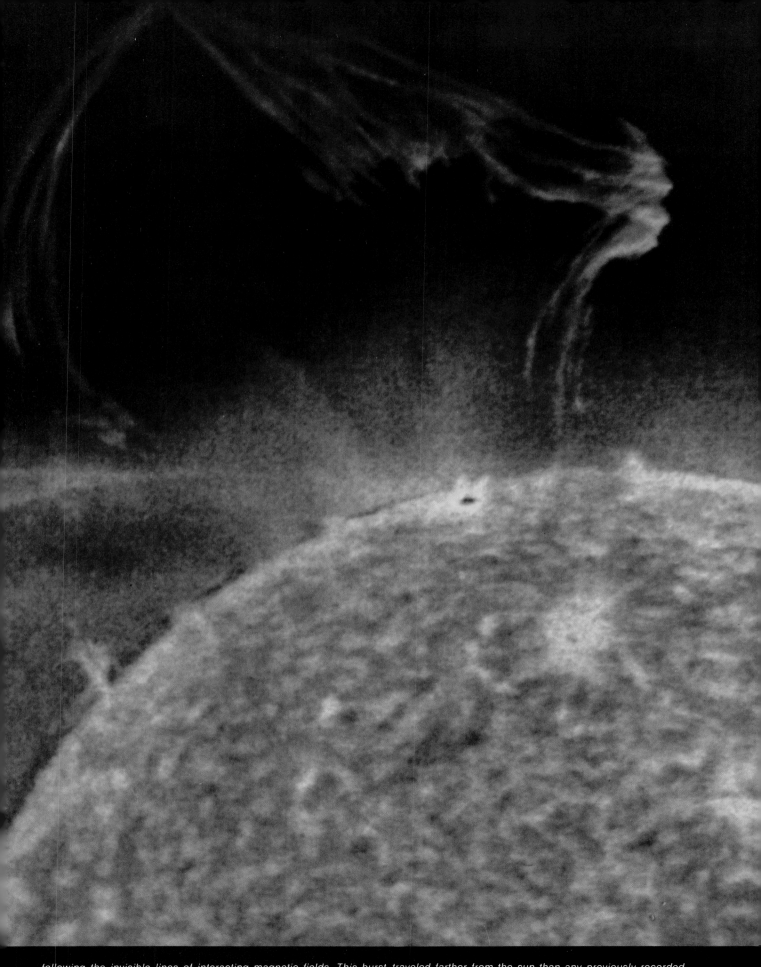

following the invisible lines of interacting magnetic fields. This burst traveled farther from the sun than any previously recorded.

The Changing View of Earth's Own Star

Although scientists will be sifting through Skylab's mass of solar observations for years to come, some results already are challenging old ideas. Discoveries in the data now analyzed have caused notions about the workings of earth's stellar neighbor to be rethought—and in some cases shelved altogether.

Prior to the Skylab missions that produced the startling photographs on the preceding pages, almost the only pictures of the sun were those taken through the earth's soupy atmosphere. These views were amplified by rocket-made snapshots and a few vague images sent back by unmanned satellites, whose small size did not allow sophisticated instruments of the kind carried on Skylab. With this limited evidence—plus a great deal of mathematical deduction—astronomers had relied upon the model of the sun sketched in the cutaway opposite: a hot globe of gas that is layered like an onion, with temperatures and pressures generally decreasing as the distance from the core increases. Its overall outlines have been confirmed by Skylab, but many details were shown to be oversimplified.

The sun's core is thought to be a gigantic thermonuclear furnace, in which the continuous fusion of hydrogen atoms into helium generates temperatures of 15 million degrees centigrade and pressures 250 billion times greater than atmospheric pressure at the earth's surface. In a zone perhaps 30,000 to 60,000 miles below the surface, solar gases begin to seethe and, like porridge in a pot, churn energy toward the surface. Just above this convection zone is a thin shell of gases about 250 miles thick, called the photosphere, which emits most of the sun's visible light. Temperatures here are among the coolest on the sun, some 6,000° C. Above this layer is the chromosphere, 6,000 miles thick, and above it the sun's outer atmosphere, or corona.

The chromosphere and corona have provided some of the chief solar puzzles, for there the idea of a neat solar onion, with its hot core and gradually cooler layers, breaks down. Temperatures soar from a few thousand degrees centigrade in the photosphere to 100,000° in the chromosphere and to two million in the corona.

Although Skylab's telescopes, like previous instruments, could not reach into the sun's interior, they did turn up some clues about the sun's outer regions. Among other things, Skylab has strengthened scientists' doubts about sharply divided onion-like layers, each with uniform characteristics, throughout the sun's thickness.

The first notion to be discarded was that of a quiet corona, one that does not vary much from section to section. In its place is a corona that boils with energy and is holed all over like Swiss cheese. These holes, in an area that had been thought to be fairly uniform gas, also have led to a new view of the solar wind—the stream of electrically charged gas particles that the sun emits.

At first solar wind was thought to result from an expanding corona. Now scientists believe that high-speed spurts of solar wind originate near the surface of the sun, where fragmented magnetic fields channel solar particles through the coronal holes, much as a nozzle channels water from a hose. There is a kind of reverse evidence for the magnetic fragmentation in the numerous looplike structures, photographed by Skylab in areas where there are no coronal holes; the loops seem to show what happens when the magnetic fields are not fragmented. The Skylab pictures suggest that the loops are hot gas particles trapped by complete magnetic fields before gases escape to become solar wind.

Skylab has apparently verified scientists' suspicion that the division of corona and chromosphere into two zones was not nearly so distinct as the simple model of the sun indicated. Rather, both parts of the solar atmosphere mix together at their boundary in a mass of swirling gases and rapidly changing temperatures and pressures. This transition region seems to consist almost entirely of electrically charged atoms of carbon and nitrogen. Since it is a mixture of material from both zones, it should possess temperatures, scientists had thought, ranging from 100,000° C. (the upper limit in the chromosphere) to one million degrees (the lower limit in the corona). When Skylab recorded the sun by taking pictures of its ultraviolet light, which is emitted by gases at these superhot temperatures, the images indicated just the heat properties the scientists had predicted for such a transition region.

Many of the questions that Skylab answered about the sun, while satisfying, are probably less interesting to the astronomer than the new puzzles it turned up. One was the discovery that the solar disc is speckled nearly all over with bright points—far more than the few that were detected by rocket-borne cameras along the solar equator in 1969. Skylab showed these points evolving on the disc. Some changed rapidly, growing 10 times brighter in less than a minute.

The proliferating points inspired a number of speculations. "It's like discovering a new animal in the forest that may turn out to be an important species," commented John Eddy of the High Altitude Observatory in Boulder, Colorado. Some astronomers think the new species is the forebear of solar flares. Giuseppe Vaiana of the Harvard College Observatory relates the bright points to the results of internal solar action, and proposes that turbulence in the convection zone pumps energy outward into the points.

Such venturesome ideas are typical of the theories and deductions stimulated by the new facts Skylab has delivered. By adding to and sharpening the questions men have asked about the sun since ancient times, it has moved astronomers closer to the goal of understanding the blazing globe that supports all life on this planet.

ARTHUR FISHER

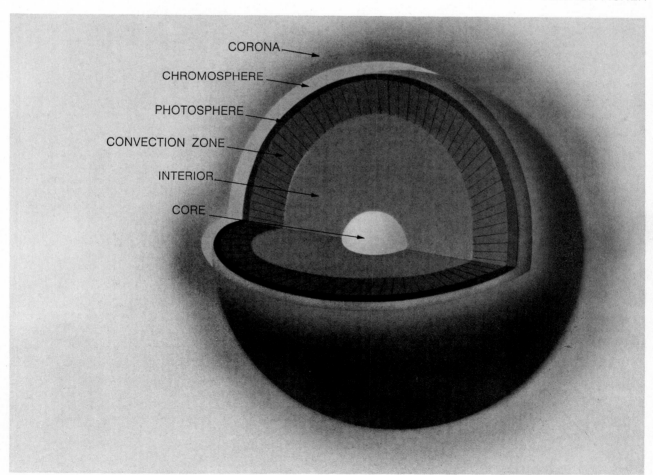

This traditional "onion" model of the sun is based on a superhot core, which began burning six billion years ago. Energy from the core swirls up through the less dense interior to the convection zone, where it is transferred to the surface, or photosphere, the source of most visible sunlight. In the chromosphere and the uppermost region, the corona, temperatures jump to some two million degrees centigrade, an increase that still baffles astronomers.

A Viking Village in America

RELICS OF 1000 A.D. PROVE NORSE SETTLED IN CANADA

by Robert Wallace

With barely a trace of embarrassment Yale University announced in January 1974 that its famous Vinland Map, which scholars had called "the most exciting cartographic discovery of the century," was a fake. The map, purporting to show part of the New World as it had been discovered by Norsemen long before Columbus, turned out to be drawn in ink that could not have been manufactured before the 1920s. The melancholy fact was determined by a Chicago testing laboratory, which subjected tiny specks of the ink to complex analysis; there was no question about the finding: 20th Century ink on 15th Century paper.

Although the identity of the forger was not revealed, it appears that he may have been a European, scholarly of mind and skillful of hand, who obtained some blank paper—perhaps end papers from a book of manuscripts—manufactured at a Swiss mill around 1433. On this he drew a map of Europe as earlier, medieval cartographers had known it, and in the western ocean he placed Iceland, then Greenland, and farthest west of all, a large island or small continent labeled *Vinlanda Insula* (Vinland Island). Nearby, also in Latin, he wrote that "the companions Bjarni and Leif Ericson" had "discovered a new land, extremely fertile and even having vines, which island they named Vinland."

The forged map, together with two unrelated, authentic manuscripts that once had been bound in the book with the blank end papers (old wormholes in all three matched exactly), was purchased in the 1950s for $3,500 by a New Haven rare-book dealer. Convinced that all the items were genuine, he sold them for nearly one million dollars to an anonymous buyer who in turn

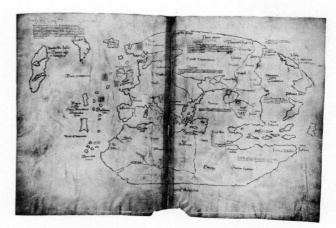

Finally exposed as fake, the forged Vinland Map had been hailed as proof of Vikings' exploration. Complete with authentic worm-holes, it shows the New World as an island.

A Newfoundland worker, digging within a string grid that will fix the location of objects he may find, carefully scrapes earth from a Norse house site at L'Anse aux Meadows.

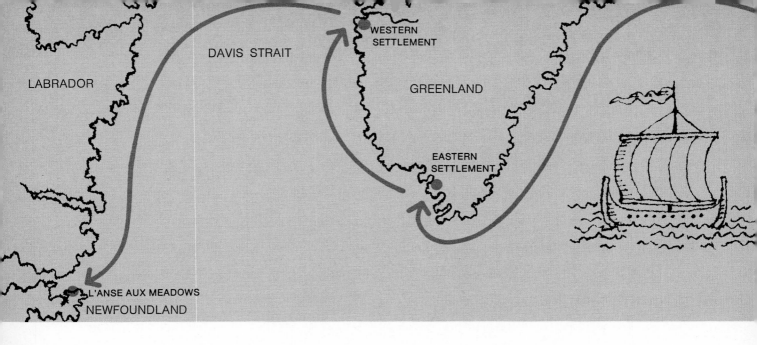

presented them to Yale. From 1965 onward, despite the quizzical tilt of a few experts' eyebrows, the Vinland Map remained the centerpiece of the university's collection. In fact Yale went so far, in all innocence, as to hornswoggle 10,000 people who paid $15 each for copies. But then the tests were made and the results announced.

No great harm was done. Yale's reputation for honest scholarship was unimpeached and the anonymous donor had already taken his tax deduction, which was valid regardless of the map's authenticity. Indeed the affair had a positive aspect: It turned attention from the fictitious to the real news about the Norse discovery of America. Every school child knew Norsemen had reached the New World 500 years before Columbus. But what had not been known is the extent of their exploration and, surprisingly, settlement.

It is now clear that Norsemen established a settlement, not merely touched ground, near the Newfoundland village called L'Anse aux Meadows and that this colony endured for several generations. There, archeologists working for Parks Canada are engaged in a three-year program to complete the excavation of this settlement before the arrival of an expected influx of tourists. It is probably not the Vinland of the old sagas, the Icelandic histories that deal with the

discovery of America, nor is there any evidence that Leif Ericson ever set foot there. But beyond doubt Norsemen were living there around 1000 A.D. No other authentic Norse site or artifact (box, pages 26-27) has yet been found in North America. The ruins at L'Anse aux Meadows provide the first archeological proof that the sagas are true, and focus renewed attention on recent reinterpretations of the sagas' value as history.

L'Anse aux Meadows—the name is probably a corruption of the French *L'Anse aux Méduses,* Bay of Jellyfish—lies at the northern tip of Newfoundland, near the Strait of Belle Isle between Newfoundland and Labrador. Drift ice and large icebergs may be seen offshore as late as July, and midsummer temperatures are now in the range of 40° to 75°, but 1,000 years ago the climate was a little warmer. To the Norsemen it must have seemed a particularly favored place. On an old beach terrace, which today lies about 15 feet above sea level, they built at least eight houses. Among them were a typical Norse longhouse, another longhouse with three additions, some smaller dwellings, a smithy and a bath house. In addition there was a pit for communal cooking, a charcoal kiln and, possibly, four or five boat sheds. If all of the houses were occupied at the same time, the settlement may have

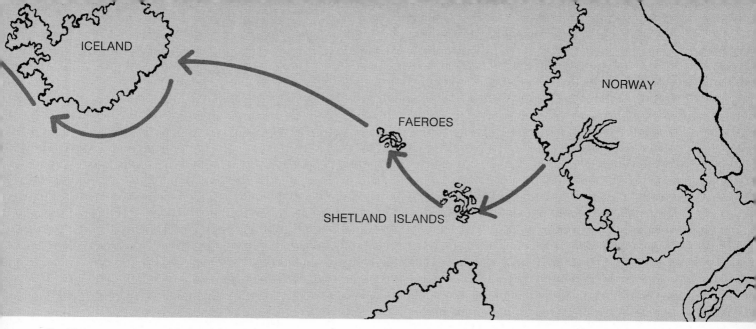

The Western Way took settlers in stages 4,000 miles from Norway to the New World. The Shetlands and Faeroes were reached by 860 A.D., Iceland by 930. In 986 Eric the Red visited Greenland, where Western and Eastern settlements were established. Around 1000, Norsemen crossed Davis Strait and coasted past Labrador to Newfoundland.

contained somewhere between 50 and 100 people—plus some livestock—who had reached there at the end of a perilous quest across the Atlantic. The discovery of the houses has made it necessary to take a new look at Norse history, ships and navigation.

During the Viking Age in the 9th and 10th Centuries, swarms of pirate vessels sailed out of the fjords of Scandinavia. The Danes went west and south to vandalize England, Ireland, Germany and France; the Swedes, after crossing the Baltic, took river routes southeast to establish the first Russian state. The Norwegians also sailed south, even into the Mediterranean, and their Viking pirates were as ferocious as any, but they had a more practical interest in the unexplored North Atlantic: They were seeking new lands that could be colonized—their farmlands were poor and becoming increasingly exhausted with each generation. Since their coastlines faced west, it was natural for them to search in that direction.

The *Vestervegen* or Western Way of the Norsemen was an island-hopping route that took them to the Hebrides, the Orkneys and the Shetlands, where colonies were established sometime in the dim years before 800 A.D. From the Shetlands the Norsemen sailed 230 miles west to the Faeroes and thence another 600 miles to Iceland,

which was settled in 874. Although it appears, at least on a map studied at ease in an armchair, that the Norsemen could have sailed all the way to the New World in this manner without ever making an individual journey longer than 1,000 miles, the Western Way was dangerous and demanded superb seamanship and navigation.

Lacking both compasses and maps, the Norsemen were among the world's most skilled at navigating from natural signs. They had no means of determining longitude but they were adept in fixing latitude by observing stars and the sun. They were students of driftwood and of floating plants. From the taste of the water they could tell where rivers flowed into the ocean. On long voyages they carried cages of birds; far at sea they released them one at a time. If the bird returned to the ship, the men knew that no land was visible. If the bird flew to the rear, they knew that their departure point was still in sight behind them. But if the bird flew forward the sailors followed it to presumably unknown land.

Recently scientists have concluded that the Norsemen also used a device similar to the twilight compass employed by airline navigators to locate the direction of the sun when it is obscured by thick clouds or even when it is below the horizon. Its operation depends on the polarization of light waves—the angle of the plane in which the waves vibrate. The compass points to the sun when its polarizing filter is properly aligned with the polarization of light coming from the direction of the sun. The Norse device, mentioned in the sagas as a "sunstone" but never clearly described, apparently was a translucent crystal of the mineral cordierite found in Scandinavia. Its molecules, like those of a modern polarizing filter, are all aligned parallel to each other. When the crystal is turned so that its natural molecular alignment is at right angles to the plane of polarized light from the sun, the color of the crystal turns from yellow to dark blue. The Danish archeologist Thorkild Ramskou, experimenting a few years ago with a lump of cordierite, found that in dense overcast he could locate the sun within two and one half degrees of its true position and track it when it had sunk as much as seven degrees below the horizon. "I now feel convinced," he said, "that the old Viking sailors with the aid of their sunstone could navigate with enormous accuracy."

As remarkable as the methods that the Vikings used in navigation were the vessels in which they sailed. In war the Norse used "dragon ships" with beasts' heads carved on their high, up-curved prows. They were built in considerable numbers and were of surprisingly large size. A fleet of 80 vessels, each carrying 100 men, is said to have been used in a single raid on Britain.

Norse ships in which Norwegian kings and queens were entombed have been unearthed in good condition at Gokstad and Oseberg. The Gokstad vessel, small for a warship, is 78 feet long and 17 feet at its greatest width. It was uncovered in 1880, after 1,000 years underground, and in 1893 a replica of it called the *Viking* was sailed across the Atlantic to be exhibited at the world's fair in Chicago.

The vessels that reached L'Anse aux Meadows were modifications of these ships, slower and sturdier craft called *knarrs*. Unlike a warship, which was propelled by both sails and oars, the knarr had only sails, square and made of tightly woven wool probably backed by cord netting. A good-sized knarr, stoutly timbered but with a canoe-like flexibility, could carry as much

as 30 tons of cargo—on a colonizing voyage, that weight might have included tow boats, a dozen men, women and children, an assortment of tethered cows, pigs and sheep, food and fodder, firewood and water for a month, plus equipment for farmers and craftsmen on board.

The westward drive of the Norsemen was so strong that, by the year 930, little more than half a century after the discovery of Iceland, all of the good land on the island had been claimed. There were 30,000 to 70,000 people there, the majority of them Norwegians, and they established an independent nation. Like the immigrants who were to pour into the United States some 900 years later, many came not only in search of land but also to escape political pressure at home, laid on by King Harald Fairhair, who unified Norway in the last part of the Ninth Century. And some, like other American arrivals, came to stay a step ahead of the law.

A BORN REAL ESTATE PROMOTER

Among the immigrants to Iceland was a latecomer named Eric the Red, who arrived around 975. A violent man, Eric had been obliged to leave Norway "because of some killings," as the sagas put it. In Iceland Eric secured a good estate through marriage but killed at least two more men; he was tried in court and sentenced to outlawry for a three-year term, which he decided to spend in exploring to the west. Iceland was full of tales of still another land that lay beyond the horizon; indeed the crew of at least one knarr, blown off course in a storm, had sighted it but had not set foot there. In 982 Eric sailed southwest and found the land, which he explored for three years. In the words of the *Saga of Eric the Red,* one of the two Icelandic sagas that deal at any length with the discovery of America, "He named the country he had discovered Greenland, for he said that people would be much more tempted to go there if it had an attractive name." Thus down the corridor of history sounds the pitch of the born real estate promoter.

Actually, to men accustomed to living in northern latitudes, Greenland was pleasant enough. Although it was treeless and its entire east coast was dangerous to approach because of ice, the southwest coast was accessible and even hospitable. There was good pasture on the narrow lowland strip between the sea and the high inland icecap; there was an abundance of seals, whales and walrus; and even if the land was not always green, it was in summer. When Eric the Red returned to Iceland and described his discovery, he was able to recruit a good many prospective colonists. In the summer of 985 or 986 he led a fleet of 25 ships, bearing perhaps 400 people and their portable property, westward toward the new land. Unhappily the fleet encountered storms and about half the ships either sank or turned back, but eventually 14 of them put in to harbors on Greenland's west coast. Two settlements were founded and the Norse bridgehead was established. (The settlements endured for nearly 500 years, expanding to a maximum of about 5,000 people, but in time the population dwindled and then disappeared—for reasons archeologists and historians still cannot explain.)

Once the Norse had settled Greenland, a journey to North America—200 nautical miles across the Davis Strait—was inevitable. It was less than 20 years before the venture took place. The *Saga of Eric the Red* and the other key Icelandic work, the *Greenlanders' Saga,* each contains varying accounts of the first successful foray on the American mainland, but scholars generally agree on some basic points. The initial landing was made about 1000 A.D. by one of Eric's sons, Leif Ericson, with a crew of 35 men. On the North American side of Davis Strait, Leif first encountered a land "where there was no grass to be seen, and the hinterland was covered with great glaciers, and between glaciers and shore the land was like one great slab of rock." In accordance with the Norse custom of naming places after local characteristics, Leif called it Helluland, which meant Flat-Stone Land or Slabland. It was the southeastern coast of Baffin Island. After a hasty look at that grim place Leif headed south and came to a country that was well wooded, with a low, cliffless coastline and white sandy beaches. He named it Markland, or Forestland, and it seems very likely that this was Labrador. Leif then continued south until he sighted an island, and beyond it a headland or cape jutting to-

ward him from what appeared to be a mainland. He landed on the cape at a place where a river flowed out of a lake into a shallow bay. Both river and lake teemed with big salmon. The climate seemed so mild to him that he thought livestock might live on the local grass all winter without requiring hay. Leif decided to spend the winter there himself, so he and his men built "some large houses" and settled in. Sometime later one of Leif's men found—according to one interpretation of the sagas—"vines and grapes" in quantity, and on this account the land was named Vinland—with a long "i," as in Wineland.

The name Vinland calls up not only Yale's map but also a controversy that has divided students for the past century. Where *is* Vinland? The only observation of Leif's that might fix the latitude translates as, "Day and night were of a more equal length there than in Greenland or Iceland. On the shortest day of winter, the sun was visible in the middle of the afternoon as well as at breakfast time." But the fix is too broad: anywhere between Newfoundland and New Jersey.

A VIOLENT ENCOUNTER IN THE NEW WORLD

Leif went back to Greenland, where his report aroused great curiosity. Soon another of Eric the Red's sons, Thorvald Ericson, borrowing Leif's ship and perhaps some of his crew, repeated the voyage. Thorvald apparently had no difficulty in finding the houses his brother had built, for he stayed in them. The landmarks of the island and the cape must have led him there. Thorvald spent two years investigating the region, finding more grapes, and then encountered some North American natives, probably Eskimos, whom he called *Skraelings* (wretches). Thorvald and his men promptly fell upon the Skraelings and killed eight out of nine of them. So much for the first meeting of Europeans and American natives. The ninth Skraeling ran to get reinforcements, and in the ensuing battle Thorvald was killed by an arrow in the armpit. His men survived, however, and returned to Greenland with the sad news.

Archeologists, both professional and amateur, have spent a good deal of time hunting for Vinland in the last century. Most of them have looked, reasonably enough, on the Atlantic coast

Norsemen in a New Land

This painting is based on archeologists' reconstruction of a Viking settlement at L'Anse aux Meadows, Newfoundland, in 1000 A.D., the only Norse outpost discovered thus far in North America. The first Norsemen would have arrived in ships like those on the beach and presumably stayed there after discovering bog iron, the ore being dug from the bank at left center. The man at the kiln across from the iron dig is making charcoal for use in smelting. In a pit nearby, the iron ore was heated with charcoal, which caused lumps of iron to separate from slag. The iron was then taken to the smithy, the cavelike structure to the right of the kiln, and forged into tools.

The working of iron—presumably for shipment to Greenland villages—was not the settlers' only livelihood. They apparently brought livestock *(center),* and the women spun wool with distaffs, spindles and "whorl" counterweights *(foreground).* The children helped out by picking berries. The house under construction at far left is typically Norse: sod walls, with roofs of roughhewn beams topped with sod that was tied down by stone-weighted ropes.

Norse artifacts found at the village of L'Anse aux Meadows in Newfoundland are reproduced here in actual size. The stone lamp was quick and easy to make and widely used. A Norse householder simply scraped a hollow in a beach pebble, filled it with seal or whale oil and inserted a wick.

The spindle whorl is a small stone weight that turns a shaft, twisting raw wool into yarn. Discovery of this one at L'Anse aux Meadows is evidence that the settlement was a real colony, including women and domestic equipment, and not merely an outpost of male explorers or traders.

within the range of wild grapes, which today are not found north of Passamaquoddy Bay in Maine. The climate was warmer by an average 5° in 1000 A.D., but even then the median summer temperature in Iceland, Greenland, Newfoundland and the other locations likely for Norse settlement was too low for wild grapes. Excellent arguments, buttressed by navigational and botanical notes, have placed Vinland in Georgia, Virginia, New York, Rhode Island and Massachusetts.

However, as long ago as 1898 a Swedish philologist, Sven Søderberg, suggested a different approach, which hinges on the pronunciation of Vinland. If it is pronounced with a short instead of a long "i," vin-land instead of vine-land, the meaning of the word is changed. It becomes "grasslands" or "fertile land." In the Old Norse language, there was indeed a short-voweled word, vin, with that meaning, which survives today in Norwegian place names, such as Vinjar and Vinås, Hovin and Bjørgvin. Leif Ericson, as his father's son, would have liked an attractive

name like Grassland. Norse colonists wanted good pasture for their sheep and cattle. The trouble with this idea, however, is that not many scholars believe in it. Modern researchers point out that vin in the sense of pasture land had passed out of existence long before Leif's time. He would probably not have heard of it.

Even if it is granted that Leif was talking about grassland, what can explain the several seemingly clear references to grapes and wine in the sagas? Are they the work of the Icelandic scribes who first put the orally preserved sagas on parchment—and also edited and added to them—two centuries after Leif's death? Or is it possible that Leif himself confused wild berries with grapes? Although he was familiar with wine obtained in trade with Europe, he may never have seen grapes—which, then as now, did not grow in Scandinavia. However, he did know all about fermentation; Norsemen were great drinkers of mead made from honey. If he encountered fermentable, wine-producing berries in the New

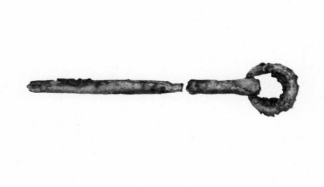

A ring-headed pin made of bronze was used to fasten a man's cape to his shoulder so that his sword arm would be free. Similar pins have also been found at Viking sites in Norway, Iceland and the Isle of Man. Archeologists can tell from its style that it was made in the 9th or 10th Century.

World, might he have called them grapes and called the place Wineland? But here, too, as in the case of the short-voweled *vin,* most scholars shake their heads. Grapes are grapes.

There is one student of the Norse discovery of America, Helge Ingstad, who believes in both heretical theories, grassland and wine berries. His belief does not make the ideas correct but he has a major advantage over more orthodox scholars: He found the settlement at L'Anse aux Meadows. Helge Ingstad, born in 1899 in Norway, was trained not as an archeologist but as a lawyer, and has served briefly as governor of Spitsbergen. But during much of his life he has been preoccupied with anthropology and exploration, and has long suspected that the Norse settlements in America were farther north than is generally believed. In the summer of 1960, while pursuing this notion along the northernmost coast of Newfoundland, Ingstad found the first sign that he had been right. He reached the isolated village of L'Anse aux Meadows,

home to 11 families of fishermen, and asked one of the elder men if there were any old ruins in the area. The man led him to a spot on the shore of Épaves Bay, half a mile southwest of the village, and pointed to the low remains of some walls. They were barely perceptible mounds, little more than palpable shadows in the grass.

Ingstad was impressed. There are no trees near the site. It is lonely pasture land today, although in Norse times it may have been well wooded. A swift, cool stream called Black Duck Brook, narrow enough in many places to be leaped, runs past the ruins. It is certainly not a river, merely a brook; but in summer, Newfoundland boys from the fishing village catch salmon in it, seizing them with quick, bare hands. The land round about is fairly flat with a few glacier-smoothed hills lying low on the horizon. The air is sweet; there are violets and strawberries in the grass, and low-bush blueberries, gooseberries and squashberries grow close by. When Ingstad inquired, the man told him that the villagers used to make wine from squashberries.

The ruins are located at the tip of the long Newfoundland peninsula. Men sailing down from the north would see Belle Isle and then the peninsula, which would have the look of a cape or headland jutting toward them from a mainland. It is tempting to match the landscape or seascape with the sagas. At times the ruins are swept by thick fog rolling in from the Atlantic, where the ice-laden, southward-flowing Labrador Current encounters the fringes of the Gulf Stream in a roil of mist. The fog advances in an irregular wall, preceded by isolated patches gliding across the water, and it is also tempting to imagine them as sailing ships coming in to the beach.

In 1961 Ingstad returned to the site with a small party of Norwegians including his wife, Anne Stine Ingstad, an archeologist who was to supervise the excavations for that year and, as it turned out, the next seven. The immediate task was to establish who had built the ruined walls. The Strait of Belle Isle had long been a thoroughfare and a fishing ground, frequented in the past 2,000 years by Dorset Eskimos and Beothuk Indians, and since the 16th Century by European and American fishermen and whalers.

A Treasury of Fakes and Fancies

For years, to the annoyance of various Italo-American organizations, amateur archeologists —many of Scandinavian descent—have been attempting to prove that it was not Columbus but the Norse who discovered America. Indeed the Norsemen did, but the only proof thus far is the settlement unearthed at L'Anse aux Meadows in Newfoundland. The hundreds of other sites, inscriptions and artifacts that have been found along the Atlantic seaboard and in the Great Lakes region are all, alas, fancies or fakes as spurious as Yale's Vinland Map *(page 17)*.

The best known of the outright fakes is the Kensington stone, found on a farm in Kensington, Minnesota, in 1898. It bears an inscription in runic (old Teutonic) letters that tells of the misfortunes of a journey of Norwegians and ''Goths'' who reached Minnesota in 1362. Although there remain many believers in the stone, its credibility has been demolished by experts, who insist that it was inscribed by the immigrant Swedish farmer who found it. Regarded by neighbors as ''a queer genius,'' the farmer had studied runic writing. When he carved the stone, though, he used 19th-Century grammar and a modern cold chisel with a standard one-inch bit.

In a separate category between outright fake and true relic is a cache of hardware that was discovered on a mining claim near Beardmore, Ontario in the 1930s. The cache, including an ax-head and a broken sword, was true Viking-Age Norse, dating from the 10th or 11th Century. But the rejoicing among scholars was shortlived—it turned out that the weapons had been brought to Canada in modern times and hidden on the mining claim by a man who hoped to (and did) get a good price for them from a museum.

Chief among harmless fancies is the Newport Tower, near the center of that city in Rhode Island. Erected sometime around 1650, the tower was studied in 1839 by a Danish antiquarian. Nothing was more probable, he concluded, than that it was a Norse baptistery, or round church, dating from the 11th or 12th Century. This notion persists, particularly among local promoters and chamber-of-commerce men in Newport; however there is nothing to support it. Archeological excavations in and around the tower, conducted in 1948-49 under the auspices of Harvard's Peabody Museum, indicate that it dates from the 17th Century. At the deepest level were found the heel print of a colonial boot and some frag-

A rusted sword from Minnesota, its brass hilt decorated with a feather pattern, was called ''medieval Norse'' by an alleged expert. It is a U.S. Navy cutlass, 1841 model.

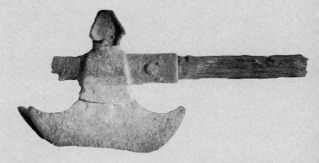

This ''halberd,'' turned up in Minnesota, where an expert said it was a ceremonial Norse weapon. It is a 19th-Century plug tobacco cutter made for a brand called Battle Ax.

ments of a clay pipe from the same period.

Because Vikings are closely associated with weapons, a good many likely looking antiques have been innocently presented as evidence of early Norse visits to America. Old-style, flared axes, of the kind used in 18th- and 19th-Century trade with the Indians, are sometimes put forward as proof, as are rusty spearheads used by French and British troops in colonial times. It often happens, too, that students in their eagerness to believe a weapon is of Viking origin, are fooled by objects of quite recent vintage—as in the cases of the "halberd" and the sword, below.

In Minnesota and nearby states, which have a large quota of citizens proud of their Scandinavian descent, many "Viking" items have been found. The local theory, which has some plausibility on a map, is that Norsemen reached the Great Lakes area by sailing into Hudson Bay, then coming south on the Nelson and Red rivers. About 40 rock drillings, as a rule an inch in diameter and five or six inches deep, have been discovered in boulders beside waterways in the region. Obviously man-made, they have been regarded as "mooring holes," into which wooden or metal pins were inserted long ago by Norse sailors securing their ships for the night. The idea is scarcely flattering to the Norsemen, for it presumes they were so stupid that they laboriously drilled holes in rocks instead of merely tying their ropes around them. In fact, the holes were drilled by 19th-Century builders who used dynamite to split boulders for house foundations, and who, for one reason or another, abandoned the holes before setting off the charges. Historians and anthropologists are not so absent-minded. Whenever someone presents them with a new Norse notion that has a hole in it, they blast it.

The runes on the Kensington stone, inscribed by a 19th-Century farmer, say in part, "8 Goths and 22 Norwegians on an exploration journey. Ave Maria, save us from evil."

The Newport Tower, a tourist attraction once ascribed to the Vikings, was originally covered with white plaster. It was probably built in the 17th Century as a lookout.

After the diggers carefully removed the grass, they began scraping a cross section through one of the walls with sharp, small, masons' trowels, skimming loose a crumbling, paper-thin sheet with each stroke. As they cut down into the nearly flattened wall it became apparent that it had been made of layers of turf, each of which originally had been two or three inches thick, but by now had been compressed to an eighth of an inch. At one time the wall had been as much as four to five feet high and four feet thick. Turf construction in that style was typically Icelandic. Such a house was the kind Norsemen might have built, but unheard-of for Indians or Eskimos.

By the end of their first summer's work, the Ingstads had discovered the remains of seven turf-walled houses. A sample of turf from one of them was dated at 1000 A.D., plus or minus 50 years. They also found several extremely corroded bits of iron, thin threads of metal inside thick rust. There were also lumps of slag, suggesting that someone long ago had been operating a smithy.

NEW WORLD NORSE SITE AUTHENTICATED

In 1962, having secured financial backing from Norwegian scientific foundations and private individuals, Ingstad returned to the ruins. To help him appraise his discovery he invited a half-dozen experts familiar with Norse culture and archeology in northern latitudes—Kristján Eldjárn, Thórhallur Vilmundarson and Gísli Gestson from Iceland; Rolf Petré from Sweden; Kari Henningsmoen from Norway; and Ian Whitaker, and William Taylor, director of the National Museum of Man, from Canada. Their unanimous opinion was that the settlement was Norse. In 1963, when the site was examined by Junius Bird of the American Museum of Natural History and Henry Collins of the Smithsonian Institution, they too were in agreement. There is no doubt about the authenticity of the ruins. They remained undiscovered for so long only because L'Anse aux Meadows was inaccessible, reachable only by boat until a gravel road was built in 1968, and because other scholars had not had Ingstad's luck.

As the site was slowly unearthed the dimensions of the houses and their floor plans became evident. One longhouse measured about 16 by 80 feet and was divided by turf partitions into four rooms; a central hearth was marked by many brittle-burned stones and deposits of charcoal. Beside it was an ember-pit like those found in ruins in Iceland and Greenland: a sunken compartment about nine by seven inches in size, lined with thin, flat stones. Glowing coals were swept into the ember-pit at night and covered with ashes, preserving the fire so that a new one would not have to be kindled in the morning. Chips of flint—jasper and iron pyrites—used in fire making were also found nearby. The roof of this house, made of turf, had apparently been supported by posts and rafters and had collapsed, covering the site. Nearby, in a location suggesting that it got there after the Norse departure, was a Dorset Eskimo arrowhead.

The remains of a few iron rivets were found near the door openings of the house. Apparently they had been used to fasten together the planks of doors that had long since fallen and vanished. As to why the Norsemen did not build the entire house of wood, which was in plentiful supply, Anne Stine Ingstad had a good answer. Turf had been the standard building material in Iceland, which they had left only a generation ago.

Another of the buildings appears to have been a second longhouse, enlarged by additions to both sides that brought its dimensions to 55 by 70 feet divided into six rooms. In one of them was found a stone lamp—a large beach pebble with a depression for oil hollowed in it—of a type common in Icelandic culture. There were more rivets, an ember-pit and several hearths, one of which contained a piece of whalebone, carbon dated at around 1025 A.D. A sample of the turf from a wall was in the same age range. The other houses on the site were all smaller, ranging down to 9 by 13 feet. One of them also showed evidence of having been occupied by Eskimos and Indians as well as Norsemen. In the bottom layer of remains was a fragment of bronze, less than half an inch long and a sixteenth of an inch wide, with ornamental cross-stripes on its face. Not far away there was a broken bone needle of a common Norse type; its eye had been cut by a metal drill. In another layer were fragments of stone tools and a piece of arrowhead or knife blade.

All seven of the dwellings were on one side of Black Duck Brook. On the opposite side, by itself, the archeologists discovered an eighth house, which had been dug partway into the bank of the stream. As they scraped down to the original floor they found a thick scattering of forging scales, particles and lumps of slag, perhaps 30 pounds of it, and a few bits of iron. The floor itself was black with charcoal that had been trodden into it; embedded firmly in the earth, protruding several inches, was a smooth, flat stone. Nearby there was a fire-blackened hearth. The house had been a smithy and the stone an anvil.

A few yards from the smithy were found the remains of a kiln, about five feet in diameter, packed with compressed charcoal. In a swampy area nearby there were rich deposits of bog iron, lying just beneath the turf in clustered, rust-red nodules as large as grapes. Norse blacksmiths, using these deposits and the charcoal, must have extracted their own iron in a smelting pit somewhere beside the stream. Although the art of smelting iron was known in the Old World more than 3,000 years ago, it was never discovered by American Indians or Eskimos. In a fairly sophisticated process, the bog ore was crushed and roasted to dry it out and remove organic matter, and then smelted at a bellows-controlled temperature of about 1200°, which separated out the iron, leaving the slag.

EVIDENCE FOR A TRUE SETTLEMENT

After two summers of digging, Ingstad and the archeologists had only a small collection of Norse artifacts: the tiny piece of bronze, the broken bone needle, the stone lamp and the rivets that had turned almost completely to rust. When the Norsemen departed they doubtless took with them everything of any use to them. Thereafter, the acidity of the soil and careful combing by Indians and Eskimos must have accounted for most of what remained. At L'Anse aux Meadows, however, at least two items of particular importance were still to be discovered.

In 1964, in a shallow exploratory trench outside the largest house, the diggers turned up a washer-shaped object made of soapstone. About an inch and a half in diameter and half an inch thick, with a hole in the center the diameter of a pencil, it was a spindle whorl. Its use in cloth-making was to act as a small flywheel, its weight giving steady momentum to a finger-spun wooden shaft that twisted raw wool into yarn. The spindle whorl was of a type common in Scandinavia in the Viking Age and later. A couple of assumptions could be based on it: that the settlement had not been an all-male outpost but had included women, and that the Norsemen had brought sheep with them. When excavation had been going on for seven summers, another dramatic find was made. Near a hearth in the longhouse, where it had been trodden into the earth floor, an archeologist found a ring-headed pin of bronze, two and three quarters inches long. This pin, used to fasten men's cloaks to their shoulders so that their sword arms would be free, was undoubtedly Norse. The style places it in the 9th or 10th Century, earlier than the settlement, but it could well have been made in Norway and taken 100 years to travel to the end of the Western Way.

Ingstad and his wife completed their excavations in 1968, but work has continued at L'Anse aux Meadows ever since. To supervise it, an international commission was established in 1972 with members from Canada, Iceland, Norway, Denmark and Sweden. Canada has designated the Norse settlement a National Historic Site and visitors have begun to make their way to it. The site is not yet overrun—a small airport nearby is often closed by Newfoundland fogs, and the only road north to L'Anse aux Meadows is gravel for the last 270 miles. But the road is scheduled to be hard-surfaced within the next few years.

In the summer of 1974 three scientists and a crew of a dozen Newfoundlanders were reexamining the ground excavated by the Ingstads and were enlarging it—the Ingstads had dug only about 2,000 square yards of the central settlement area, which contains about 6,500. The archeologist in charge, Dr. Bengt Schonback of Sweden, thought that all the sizable structures on the site had been excavated. ''But,'' he said, ''a good deal remains to be learned about the land formation at the time—whether there were bogs, and if there were, what waste material might have been preserved in them.'' The largest of the dumps or middens appears to be located in a peat-bog area between the dwellings and the shore of the bay. The Ingstads had not dug into it and Schonback was optimistic about what might be found there. He was also anxious to excavate, before the end of the digging season in 1975, all parts of the site that may be damaged by tourists. Since the site is not visually dramatic, he proposes that some replicas of the Norse houses be built nearby. The work can be done by craftsmen from Iceland, where turf houses were still being built as late as 1940.

Several questions about L'Anse aux Meadows remain to be answered, although it is likely that no complete answers will ever turn up. One question concerns the carbon dating of the samples taken from the site, 16 in all. The two samples of turf and the piece of whalebone fit perfectly with the date of the Norse expeditions to Vinland—around 1000 A.D. However, 13 samples of charcoal taken from various houses, cooking pits, the smithy and the kiln, have an average date about 100 years earlier. The oldest date is 640, plus or minus 130 years. Probably the discrepancy is accounted for by the fact that driftwood from Épaves Bay would have been useful as firewood scores or even hundreds of years after the deaths of the trees from which it came. Since carbon dating counts age from the death of the wood and not from the time it was burned, these samples from the Norse hearths would not tally with the date of occupation.

Other questions involve the general nature of the settlement. What were the Norsemen doing there? Were they attracted to the site because of the superb hunting and fishing once available? Did they choose the place because it afforded fine pasture for their livestock? Was L'Anse aux Meadows a base or way station for further explorations? How long did the Norsemen live there and what caused them to leave?

Sweden's Schonback, who is not persuaded that L'Anse aux Meadows is Leif Ericson's Vinland, was particularly curious about changes that have taken place in the contour and elevation of the land in the past 1,000 years. Studies of plant pollens, taken from core samples drawn from bogs in the area, indicate that the vegetation has not changed much during that time, although the forests have been cut back from the sea for a few miles. The accumulation of new topsoil above the ruins had been slight—little more than one inch. But the land itself has been uplifted by an unknown amount, perhaps several feet. Today Épaves Bay is very shoal. Even a shallow-draft knarr could not be beached near the settlement. But if the land was lower and the bay deeper 1,000 years ago, the site would have been more attractive to seafaring men than it is now. Schonback hopes to discover how and when bogs were formed by studying the microscopic remains of diatoms, algae whose cell walls contain silica. The remains of diatoms that once lived in salt water, brackish water and fresh water are different in appearance, and hence may provide clues to the former contours of the bay area.

A TINY INDUSTRIAL CENTER?

But even if Norsemen could have brought their ships closer to shore, perhaps within the partial protection of the bank near the mouth of Black Duck Brook, the site would have been far from the best in the vicinity. Better ones, available nearby, are now occupied by the villages of Quirpon, Griquet and the town of St. Anthony. Why then did the Norsemen settle where they did?

In Schonback's view the Norsemen may indeed have built houses in other, better locations nearby. Their ruins may never be discovered precisely because of that; today's villages lie on top of them. But there must have been a compelling reason for them also to establish a settlement on a second-best site, and Schonback suspects this may have been the presence of the bog iron and ample wood for charcoal. Possibly L'Anse aux Meadows was a tiny industrial center that supplied iron to other communities. This is only a guess, like a dozen others that scientists have made about the place, but an intriguing one. As to how long the site may have been occupied, Schonback thinks that two or three generations might be a fair estimate—long enough for men and women to have died and been buried there. He has only modest hopes of finding them, but near the ruins he is searching for the first European graves at the end of the Western Way.

Today, the site of the Norse settlement overlooks an icy sea even in June, but the climate was gentler in 1000 A.D. This view looks north across Épaves Bay to the way the Norsemen came—on the Labrador Current past Great Sacred Island—to make their landfall in the New World.

Recording the Dawn of Life

Today almost everyone thinks he knows how babies are made. But the process takes place inside the complex tubes and interconnections of the female reproductive system, and until recently, there was no visual record of this most magnificent and fateful of all biological activities. Now, thanks to a series of unique films, life's beginning has been traced and permanently recorded.

The most ambitious of these new films was released in 1974 by Japanese gynecologist Motoyuki Hayashi. To get his startling pictures of reproduction, Hayashi relied mainly on instruments known as endoscopes—pencil-thin tubes containing glass fibers and lenses that convey images from internal cavities to cameras outside. By using endoscopes, Hayashi was able to obtain some remarkable footage. Ripe eggs are shown exploding through the oval ovary that produces them (page 34), colliding with sperm to be fertilized, and moving down the tube of the oviduct to the uterus, the muscular organ where the fertilized egg grows into a fetus waiting to be born. Where the probing endoscope might harm a human fetus, Hayashi focused instead on similar stages of development in monkeys or rabbits, whose reproductive organs are like those of humans.

Hayashi's film looks like a kind of real-life *Fantastic Voyage.* Long tails twitching, sperm line up in a massive phalanx; then they attack the egg with such force that it begins to spin. What seems to be a shimmering blue spaceship hovering over a white planet is actually an egg floating above the oviduct, whose hairlike projections, or cilia, will shortly suck it inside. And soon a new life is under way.

In his Tokyo clinic, Motoyuki Hayashi prepares to insert an endoscope into the abdominal cavity of an anesthetized rabbit. This special tube, with a camera attachment, allows Hayashi to photograph the beginnings of mammalian life.

One egg (top) must combine with one of hundreds of struggling sperm (bottom) to start a new life. The egg is girdled by a dark green mass of specialized ovary cells—follicle cells—as well as a more diffuse layer of blue-green ovary cells. The mature sperm, their tails drooping down, here cluster within the male reproductive tissue. Like salmon, sperm must swim against fluid currents in the oviduct in order to reach their destination—the egg.

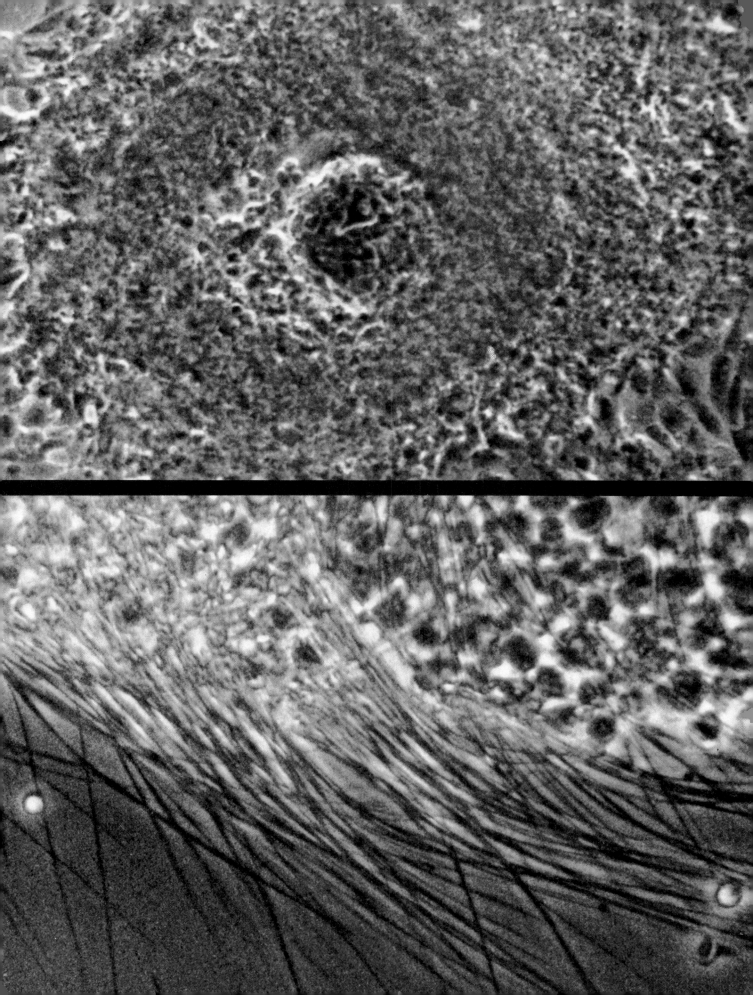

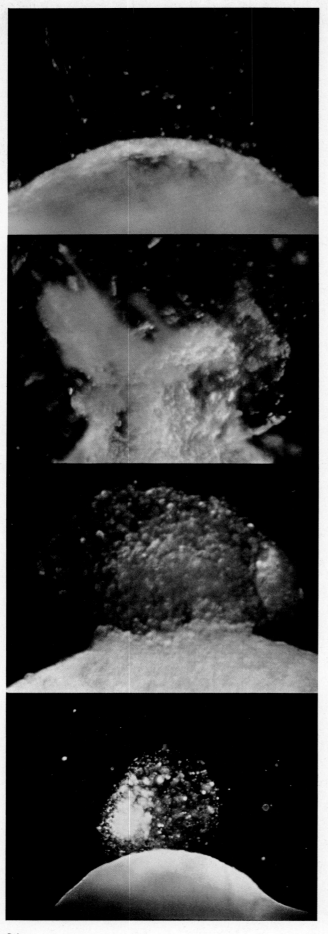

Magnified hundreds of times, the surface of the ovary bulges as the egg inside ripens. The redness is caused by blood vessels that hemorrhage just before ovulation.

Like a volcano erupting, the ovary spews out follicular cells and fluid. Scientists believe that the rupture of the ovary is caused either by the pressure of fluids around the egg or perhaps by enzymes that dissolve the thin ovary wall.

The "cloud around the egg"—cumulus oöphorus—rises in a loose greenish globule above the ruptured ovary. This step in the sequence occurs just before the egg is expelled.

Instants later, the mature egg pops out, obscured by the remaining cumulus mass on its surface. The cumulus nourishes and protects the egg as it travels to the oviduct.

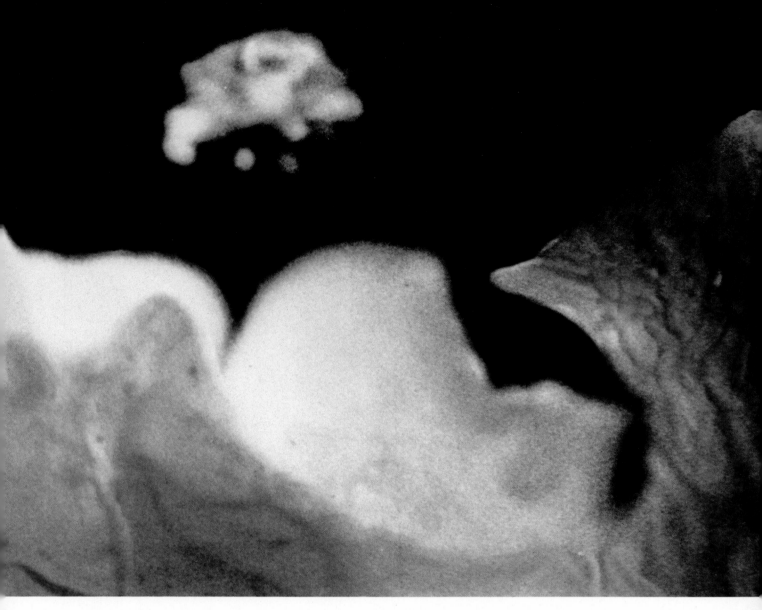

Floating eerily in inner space, the egg is about to be sucked into the fimbriae—finger-like extensions at the oviduct entrance.

Explosive Start of a Hazardous Journey

At the beginning of a truly fantastic voyage, the ripe egg (black dot) starts from its position in the ovary, explodes out of it (sequence opposite), and then begins to float freely (arrows) across the narrow gap separating the ovary from the tulip-like opening of the oviduct (second dot). Although the distance from ovary to oviduct is a mere inch, the egg —which has no means of steering itself—needs all the assistance it can get to make the passage safely. This help is provided by a unique mechanism in the oviduct, slender cilia whose beating motion sucks the egg into the tube. If the egg should miss the entrance of the oviduct after it leaves the ovary—as happens on rare occasions—it will become lost in the abdominal cavity, and the opportunity for the creation of a new life is foreclosed.

OVIDUCT   OVIDUCT

FIMBRIAE   FIMBRIAE

UTERUS

OVARY   OVARY

On its first day in the oviduct, the egg is pummeled by a mass of sperm, which set the egg whirling. In this photograph, magnified about 400 times, the sperm are visible as a ragged bluish halo that surrounds the egg.

Within 30 hours after fertilization takes place, the egg cleaves into two cells (white clumps) as it moves along the duct wall, which appears as a series of light blue ridges.

Caught by Hayashi's special camera some 10 hours later, the egg has divided into four cells and seems to nestle in a curve of one of the ridges of the muscular oviduct.

The egg reaches the uterus three days after fertilization. By then it has multiplied into a mottled, multicellular mass, but is still no larger than it was when it left the ovary.

A Chancy Encounter Between Egg and Sperm

Once it has arrived safely inside the oviduct, the egg (black dot, far right) rolls along (arrows), prodded both by ciliary action and by contractions of the muscular walls of the oviduct, until it finally enters the uterus. It is normally fertilized during the first third of its voyage through the oviduct. The egg lives only 12 to 24 hours and thus must be successfully penetrated by a single sperm within this limited time span. Once the egg is fertilized, it becomes impermeable to the other sperm. Then the egg begins to fissure, forming, as it travels, a complex mass of cells. These cells, in turn, will begin to migrate and clump together to start the development of the brain, spinal cord, heart and other human organs.

OVIDUCT

OVIDUCT

FIMBRIAE

UTERUS

FIMBRIAE

OVARY

OVARY

At the end of its journey, the egg touches the wall of the uterus, where it will implant itself and begin rapid development.

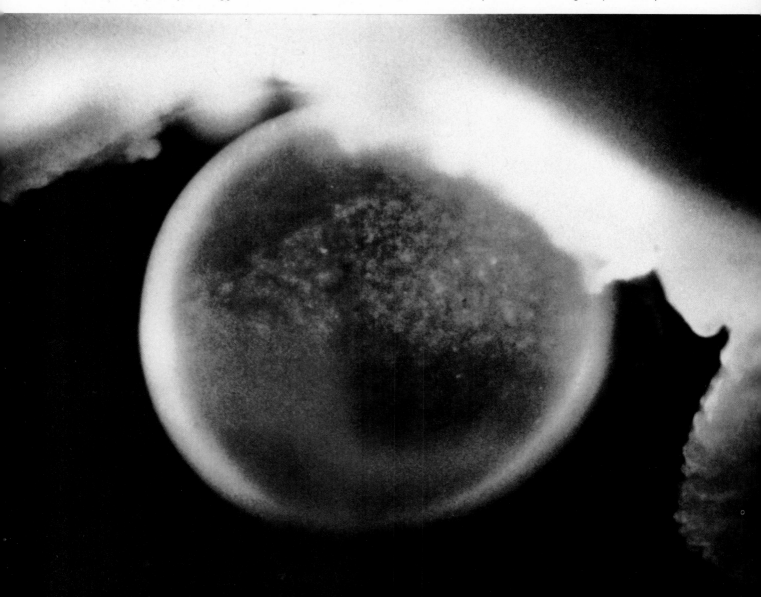

The Final Act: Shaping a Human Form

Although safe and snug in the uterus at the end of its journey, the egg (black dot) is hardly dormant. It penetrates the uterus wall and develops the structure that will see it through the final stages of its growth—the placenta, which filters, regulates and meters wastes and life-sustaining nutrients flowing between the egg (now called the embryo) and mother. While this mechanism works around the clock, the embryo undergoes a rapid and startling change. Within three weeks, a spinal cord and heart begin to take shape (below). After about two months of growth in the wall of the uterus a recognizable human fetus like the one at right has developed, and seven months later a baby is ready to be born.

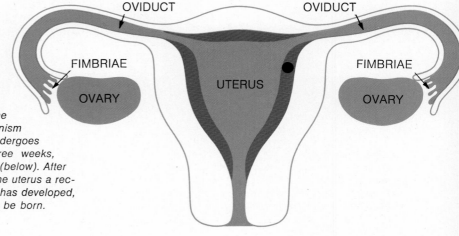

One of the first organs to develop is the heart, the grayish, bean-shaped protuberance at right, already beating steadily some three weeks after fertilization has occurred.

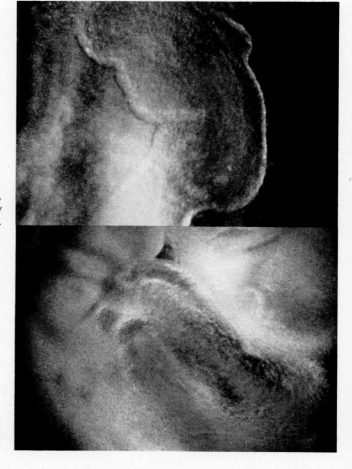

A week later, the translucent embryo is discernible, its head (top right) resting on the blood-filled heart. The orange fingers running from the heart are primitive blood vessels.

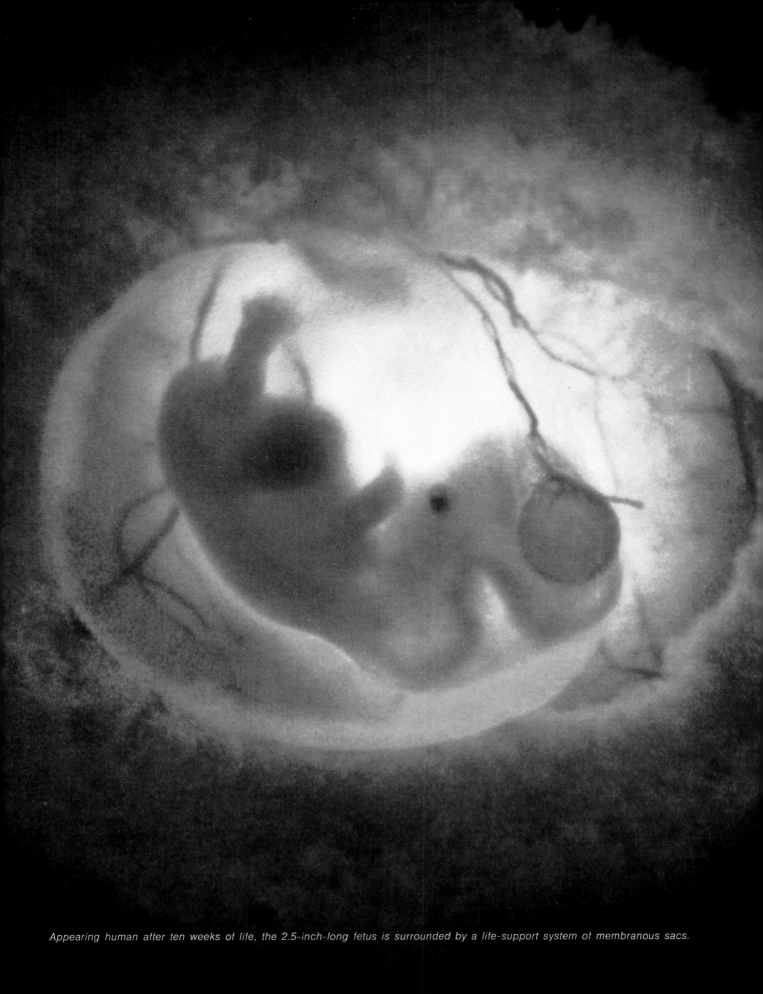

Appearing human after ten weeks of life, the 2.5-inch-long fetus is surrounded by a life-support system of membranous sacs.

New England's New Coyote

A DISTINCT RACE EVOLVES TO FIT A CHANGING LANDSCAPE

by Ogden Tanner

Right here in New England, in the latter half of the 20th Century, a brand new animal has arrived, one that has come to us when many others are disappearing and that is found nowhere else in the world. He is fascinating to watch, not only for his beautiful wildness, but also for his co-existence and interdependence with man. He seems to be filling a special ecological niche as part of a natural landscape that is actually in better balance, wilder, than it was 100 years ago.''

The speaker is Raymond P. Coppinger, associate professor of biology at Hampshire College in Amherst, Massachusetts. Coppinger and a team of undergraduate and graduate students have been attempting to capture and study an animal that seems to be defying the laws of nature —or at least the laws of nature as laid down by 20th Century man. For, in an age when the wolf faces extirpation, when the Western coyote is under murderous pressure from sheep ranchers, and when at least one of the world's species is becoming extinct every year, a new type of creature has evolved in an area that is not generally thought of as a home for wilderness animals —New England and the rest of the Northeast. While the details are not yet clear, this newcomer may be trying to tell us something about the adaptability and tenacity of all wild creatures and about the way nature has of restoring equilibrium in the wake of disturbance and change.

From the outset, the appearance of the new animal baffled woodsmen and wildlife experts alike. The first question was: What was it? Unraveling that mystery has taken nearly two decades and the best efforts of several professional biologists. To coordinate those efforts, the first region-wide conference of state and university scientists was

An Eastern coyote, trapped in upstate New York, looks like its western cousins, but closer examination shows the larger size and darker coat that mark it a new race.

called for the winter of 1975 to consider the mysterious newcomer—its lineage, its habits and how it got to the Northeast.

As early as 1912, records had indicated occasional sightings of what were described as "bush wolves" or "coyotes" in upper New York State. But it was not until the late 1950s that persistent stories of a strange new creature—apparently a wild canine—began circulating farther east and south, in Vermont and New Hampshire, in Maine, and down into Massachusetts and northwestern Connecticut. There were reports, also, of a few sporadic sightings in northern Pennsylvania, New Jersey and even Virginia.

Initially it was thought that the animals were coyotes that had been brought back from the West by tourists and had escaped or been released; some of them probably were. Many observers believed that the animals were the result of mating between coyotes and domestic dogs, and the term coy-dog was coined. While the appearance of some of the odd-looking canines tended to support this theory, no one was really sure. Assuming that the animals, whatever they were, had to be some sort of threat to livestock and deer, most farmers and hunters shot them on sight and asked questions afterward.

As for wildlife biologists, they seemed willing to agree on only one thing: the animals were not werewolves, as some newspaper stories had gleefully suggested. Now, the evidence indicates that they are not Western coyotes, wolves or coy-dogs either, but a new canine race—larger than the Western coyote, smaller than the wolf—that has evolved in an area where no such animal had lived before to fill an ecological niche that was empty and waiting for it.

How could such a race evolve? In North America, canines, the genus *Canis,* are generally recognized as embracing three distinct species: *Canis lupus,* the wolf; *Canis latrans,* the coyote; and *Canis familiaris,* the domestic dog. Within each species there is considerable variation; wolves and coyotes each exhibit differing characteristics of size and color depending on their particular habitat, and the domestic dog has been so selectively bred for different purposes over thousands of generations that it now varies

This female New Hampshire coyote and an English pointer produced a hybrid (below), biological evidence generally accepted as demonstrating the Eastern coyote is a new race.

Hybrid pups like the one at left closely resemble their domestic sire (right), not coyotes, indicating that Eastern coyotes are not simply chance offspring of wild dogs.

from toy dogs such as the tiny Chihuahua to rescue animals like the powerful St. Bernard.

Despite such differences, the wolf, the coyote and the dog, unlike most other species within a given genus, are each made up of cells containing the same number of compatible chromosomes, the cell's heredity-controlling material. Only if the number of chromosomes are identical can similar animals interbreed to produce fertile offspring. If the number of chromosomes differs, interbreeding yields sterile offspring as it does in the case of the mule, which is a cross between horse and donkey. Being sterile, mules cannot found a race of their own. But canines can. At least theoretically they can crossbreed to produce offspring that are not sterile and thus establish a new line, or race.

A RARE PIECE OF LUCK: FIVE PUPS IN A DEN
The first major study to support the theory that the "mystery animal" was a self-perpetuating new canine race and not simply an occasional hybrid was carried out by biologists Helenette and Walter Silver of the New Hampshire Fish and Game Department, working along with Barbara Lawrence and William Bossert of Harvard University and the help of a grant from the National Science Foundation. Various reports of a wolf-like animal had trickled in to the Silvers. A night snowplow operator had spotted one near Newport, New Hampshire; men on snowshoes had followed the tracks of four such creatures near the village of Croyden, a few miles north. But the trackers were not able to find the den until one of them happened to notice fresh dirt on the snow next to the footprints. Reasoning that the animals had emerged from a den and shaken off the dirt, the men backtracked along the prints and discovered the coyotes' hiding place. Inside were five pups, three females and two males. It was a rare piece of luck. When the Silvers heard about it, they asked the state Fish and Game officials to give them custody of the litter.

The Silvers took the week-old pups to their house near Boscawen, New Hampshire, where the pups became the nucleus of a project that eventually unraveled the mystery of their origin. Over the next six years, from 1960 to 1966, the Silvers observed the original five and 50 of their descendants. For purposes of comparison, the biologists also studied Western coyotes, a Canadian wolf and a few hybrids, the offspring of the New Hampshire animals and domestic dogs.

During the course of the study, it became apparent that the New Hampshire canines had characteristics of physique and behavior in common with both coyotes and wolves but had little similarity to dogs. The pups, nearly black at birth, developed a tawny, coyote coloring as they matured, but remained darker than coyotes, with dark-tipped hairs along their backs, dark vertical stripes down their forelegs, and tails tipped with black. While smaller than wolves, they were half again as heavy as the Western coyotes—averaging close to 45 pounds for males compared to 29 for the western animals, and 39 pounds for females compared to 23. They also had larger feet, blunter muzzles and bigger bones.

The Silvers reared some of the pups in the house as pets and discovered that they were every bit as affectionate as domestic dogs, although they tended to play rough. When seeking attention, they approached the Silvers, looked up into their faces and waved their tails in a graceful, side-to-side motion rather than the rapid wagging common to dogs. But their behavior with their fellow animals, as distinguished from relationships with humans, resembled that of

Two Eastern coyote pups, found in a New Hampshire forest in 1972, playfully nuzzle each other. They were destroyed by the Fish and Game people as troublesome pests.

wolves and coyotes more than that of dogs.

By the time the pups were six weeks old a definite social system had begun to reveal itself and it was very similar to that within a wolf pack or a Western coyote group. An order of dominance developed and the lowest position in this order was filled first: in each group there was inevitably one pup that was consistently picked on or accorded the least attention. The second position filled was that of the leader—invariably the boldest or most inquisitive animal in its group. As is the case among wolves and coyotes, interestingly enough, dominance was not determined by sex or size; in 10 groups of animals of similar age, a male was dominant in five and a female in five. In one group the dominant member was the smallest female; in another it was the smaller of two males. The dominant animals, as in wolf packs, carried their tails higher than other members of the group; they asserted their status by standing with their forefeet on the shoulders or belly of a submissive animal, which sat, lay or crouched in front of the dominant one, sometimes reaching up to take the "victor's" jaws gently in its own as a gesture of concession. Such ritual behavior seemed sufficient to avoid serious conflict.

The greatest difference between these New Hampshire animals and domestic dogs was their family behavior. Unlike male dogs, which are generally promiscuous and pay little or no attention to their offspring, the New Hampshire canine males were, like wolves and coyotes, monogamous and exemplary fathers.

For a week or so before the birth of a litter, and later while the female was nursing, the male deferred to his mate, allowing her to finish what food she wanted before taking any for himself. During birth, the father stood guard or paced nervously back and forth; afterward he joined the mother in licking the pups to keep them clean and in cleaning up the floor of the pen. In one litter, the Silvers noticed, the father paid particular attention to two of his weaker offspring, pushing them closer to the mother for nursing and later carrying food to them. When these pups were threatened by stronger brothers or sisters, he growled protectively, making sure the weaker ones were allowed to feed. This father also spent a great deal of time playing with his pups and as they grew older took part in the puppy game of stalking birds and butterflies that happened to fly into the pen.

SINGING ALONG WITH THE SILVERS

When these New Hampshire wild canines were about two months old they joined in howling with other members of the group, including the coyotes and hybrids, happily singing along with fire whistles, ambulance sirens, music and the Silvers themselves. Their voices, the Silvers noted, were lower in pitch than the coyotes', but higher than the wolves'. Usually there was some yapping at the start, less than among coyotes but more than among wolves. The wild animals did not bark like dogs, although some made a sort of chuffing sound as a warning that something out of the ordinary was taking place.

As their study progressed, the Silvers noted that, in some ways, the wild canines behaved more like wolves than coyotes. They displayed greater tolerance of their brothers and sisters at all ages, and some even attempted to take care of pups that did not belong to them. Their breeding pattern, moreover, indicated that some wolf genes might well be present. Both coyotes and wolves, males and females, come into heat once a year, mating in January or February and producing young about two months later. But while coyotes generally reach sexual maturity when they are about a year old, the New Hampshire animals appeared to mature at 18 months or so, closer to the two-year-old maturity of wolves.

All these facts pointed to a coyote-like animal with some wolf ancestry. But it did not rule out the possibility that the canine's characteristics were simply the result of a coyote or wolf mating with any of a variety of dogs. The first evidence to determine the coyote's ancestry came from repeated breeding experiments. The Silvers found that their original litter bred "true" through seven litters; that is, it provided pups of generally uniform characteristics. They exhibited some variability in individual appearance, but none was a "throwback"—no pup was just like a wolf or a coyote or, most important, like a dog. This fact indicated that the New Hampshire canines had become a pure strain, not simply chance hybrids of dogs. They made up a race of their own. And it seemed that this race had no dogs among its relatives. The evidence again came from breeding experiments. The Silvers had difficulty getting a wild female to mate with a domestic dog, even when they were friendly. When the two finally did mate, the resulting hybrids came into heat once a year but only in the fall, three or four months earlier than wolves and coyotes. The Silvers concluded that these hybrids would never be able to mate back to the wild side of their family. They might mate with each other, with similar hybrids or with dogs (males breed at any time). The offspring of such matches, however, would of necessity be born in the harshest months of winter, and given the fact that neither male dogs nor male hybrids assist in caring for their young, the pups' chances of survival would be slim indeed. This seemed to rule out the development of a race of coy-dogs; they would simply die out after the first generation or two. If the new race was not partly dog, it had to be largely coyote.

The Northeastern coyote of Michigan and Ontario, *Canis latrans thamnos,* the Silvers noted, already showed some evidences of wolf blood, and the Ontario wolf was small enough to mate with a coyote if pack loyalties did not prevent such a match. The Silvers and their Harvard colleagues concluded that the new animal was of predominantly coyote ancestry, but that it very likely had acquired genes from crossbreedings with wolves. In their 1969 report the biologists recommended that the new breed be designated a variety, or subspecies, of coyote, *Canis latrans var.,* with the common name Eastern coyote.

If this analysis is right, and many biologists go along with it, then the mystery animal of the Northeast has been identified. But its identity is only part of the puzzle. Because coyotes are animals of the western prairies, what is this variant doing in a very different environment—the wooded hills of New England?

The story of the Eastern coyote constitutes the latest and most intriguing installment in the saga of what has been called the cleverest predator in North America, if not the entire world. Because

This Eastern coyote shares traits of timber wolf (below) and Western coyote (bottom), but is a separate race. It is midway in size, has big paws, broad nose and dark coat.

The timber wolf, largest of the three species, weighs as much as 100 pounds. Its ears are shorter, its face broader, and its coat darker than the Eastern or Western coyote.

The Western coyote, smaller than either its Eastern cousin or the timber wolf, weighs between 20 and 40 pounds. It also has taller ears and a more pointed muzzle.

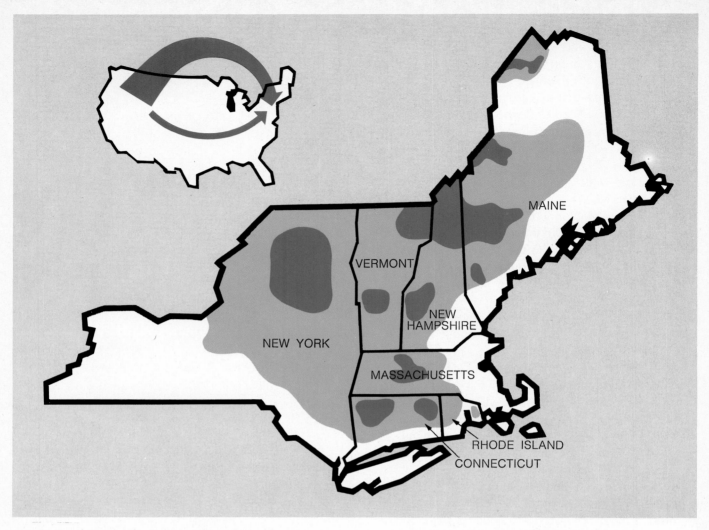

Eastern coyotes are found from Maine to New York (light shading) where they are most numerous in some woodland and farm areas (dark shading). Most are descendants of animals that migrated from the Great Plains across southern Canada (inset, heavy arrow), although some may have come east via a path south of the Great Lakes.

the coyote, virtually alone among native wild animals, has not only survived despite unbelievable persecution, but has prospered and—quite possibly pushed along by its persistent persecution—has extended its range over a great deal of North America, evolving to overcome many new conditions along the way.

Before the white man's arrival on this continent, the Indians had lived long enough with the coyote to tolerate it and, indeed, to regard it with a mixture of kinship, humor and awe. Its English name comes from the *coyotl* of the Aztec Indians, who worshiped coyote-like gods and carved their likenesses in the stones of their ancient temples. Even today old Mexican Indians delight in telling Aesop-style fables about the "smartest animal on earth." In the myths of some of the Plains Indian tribes the coyote was the first animal to be created; he then made the rest of the world and its various other creatures before calling them all together to counsel him on the creation of his masterpiece, man.

With the advent of the first settlers west of the Mississippi River, however, attitudes abruptly changed. The coyote and every other animal thought to pose a threat to life, livestock or crops —wolves, mountain lions, bears, hawks, eagles, foxes, weasels, even crows—were summarily shot, trapped, poisoned or clubbed to death as a matter of course. Since government-supported predator-control programs began in the 1930s literally millions of coyotes have been killed; the toll has exceeded that of all the remainder of the predators put together.

But unlike some of the other, larger predators, the coyote was canny and flexible enough to stay alive. It adapted its feeding habits to take advantage of the scourge of rodents that came with agriculture, and its taste for the pests helped farmers keep them in check. If the opportunity presented itself the coyote also fed on the carcasses of dead livestock as well as an occasional live chicken, lamb or calf. The virtual extermination of larger carnivores like the wolf, which were less flexible and more dependent on the larger, vanishing herbivores like bison, elk and moose, also worked to the coyote's advantage, for much direct competition for game was removed. The breed may have originally hunted by daylight and in larger packs like the wolf, then become more solitary and nocturnal after it had tasted the ranchers' wrath. By this adaptation alone the coyote may have escaped the fate of the wolf and such notoriously gregarious, and unwary, species as the bison (which very nearly reached extinction) and the passenger pigeon (which did). Certainly it was quick to learn tricks in avoiding guns, traps and hunting dogs, as well as the snowmobiles and airplanes from which it is still hunted for revenge or sport.

Originally an animal of the open plains, as its first name "prairie wolf" reflects, the coyote moved into wooded and hilly areas too. There it profited, along with deer, livestock and other animals, from the food supply offered by "edge" habitats: open glades cleared by fire or logging and flourishing with succulent new growth plus an ample supply of rabbits, mice, insects, berries and birds. Gradually coyotes penetrated into the U.S. Northwest and western Canada. Coyotes were unknown in Alaska before the Klondike gold rush of 1898 but seem to have followed the prospectors' pack trains north, perhaps drawn by castoff garbage and, toward the end of the trail, by dead and dying horses. By 1947 the coyote had become established all the way from Point Barrow in northernmost Alaska to Costa Rica and Honduras in Central America, where it

had followed the course of Spanish settlement south from Mexico centuries before, and had also moved east into Ontario and Michigan. In the course of adapting to these different new environments, Canis latrans has evolved into no less than 19 subspecies. They vary from small, slim-boned, light-colored animals suited to desert regions, to heavier, darker specimens more at home in the cool Northern evergreen woods.

AN EXTREMELY ADAPTABLE PREDATOR

The coyote, in the words of one biologist, is a superb example of a "successional" or "subclimax" animal; i.e., one that, like the white-tailed deer, can profit from human alteration of the climax, or stable, flora and fauna originally found across the greater part of the continent. It is this ability in particular that makes the appearance of such a mystery animal in the Northeast somewhat more understandable, if no less miraculous. For its advent depended on a little-recognized development in the environment of what has always been the most heavily settled and urbanized part of the country.

In the three and one half centuries since European settlers first arrived, the Northeast has gone from wilderness to intensive cultivation and back to semi-wilderness again. That cycle has had a subtle effect on wildlife: some primeval species disappeared forever, but others waned only to bounce back, and still others have arrived in places where they never lived in ancient times. The original forest cover of the region was probably not the ideal territory for a medium-sized predator like a coyote; the densest evergreen forest did not support great populations of small animals, and those that abounded in the deciduous forests and clearings, where there was tender vegetation to feed on, were prey to the wolf. The coyote, being smaller and lighter, could not successfully compete.

By the mid-19th Century the settlers had pretty well killed off the wolves or driven them north into Canada. Furthermore, through hunting, the pioneers had also seriously reduced the populations of beaver, moose, raccoon, deer and other animals on which a predator must depend; and they had destroyed a great deal of the nat-

Search for an Elusive Newcomer

The search for the Eastern coyote has more than once run afoul of the animal's cleverness and adaptability, the very attributes that enabled it to establish itself as a new species in the built-up Northeast. Attempts to capture pups for study have been frustrated by the coyote's wiliness.

Biologist Raymond Coppinger of Hampshire College in Amherst, Massachusetts and 10 students of his explored the Massachusetts and New Hampshire countryside for two winters and springs, seeking the animals. Even though the team trailed some for weeks—and spent several nights sleeping on the ground in —30° weather —the coyotes managed to stay a tantalizing jump ahead. The team did discover that the coyote's reputation as a deer killer is overrated. The only deer they found killed by a coyote had been wounded first by a hunter's bullets.

Near Mount Washington in New Hampshire, students uncover the remains of a deer that escaped the hunter who had shot it—and later provided a meal for a coyote.

Clues to the size of the elusive Eastern coyote are gained by measuring the distance between tracks in the snow.

Concealed by underbrush, an abandoned coyote's den was discovered in the spring of 1974 near Worthington, Massachusetts.

Using Poison to Save Coyotes

The battle between ranchers and ecologists over the fate of the Western coyote—ancestor of the new race in the Northeast—may be settled amicably by a new method that makes them leave livestock alone but does not kill them.

Total eradication of coyotes had been called for by sheep and cattle raisers who insisted that the predators destroyed their herds. Ecologists claimed that the spring-loaded tubes filled with cyanide used to destroy coyotes killed other species too. This argument convinced the government in 1972 to ban the use of all poison for predator control, but in May 1974 ranchers succeeded in getting the ban lifted. Now a new way of poisoning may spare both the coyote and its prey. Psychologists Carl Gustavson of Eastern Washington State College and John Garcia of UCLA explain their idea: "If an animal ate a meal that made it sick, it would avoid that kind of meal in the future." To verify this concept they fed lamb meat, injected with a mild poison called lithium chloride and wrapped in fresh lamb hide, to seven coyotes. All the animals became violently ill and, after repeated "conditioning," avoided live lambs although they readily attacked and ate other prey.

The researchers discovered that coyotes repeatedly sickened by their natural prey apparently acquire a permanent dislike for such meat and, in some cases, are terrified by the mere sight of the animals.

Ultimately, the scientists hope that later generations of coyotes will learn from their poison-treated mothers to avoid attacking sheep. Such conditioning, contend Gustavson and Garcia, "would save the lambs . . . while allowing coyotes and other predators to roam the wild country as they have for the past million years."

ural environment for both predator and prey by clearing vast sections of wilderness for pastures and farms. At this time, many parts of New England, which were originally 90 per cent or more forested, had become three-quarters cultivated fields and only a quarter woods.

By the late 19th Century, however, the waves of settlement had lapped up the hillsides and ebbed. Hundreds of thousands of New Englanders—pushed by the dislocations of the Civil War, by the opening of the Erie Canal and the railroads, and by the availability of richer, more fertile land out West—abandoned their rocky, hard-won holdings. Their fields and pastures, so painstakingly cleared of trees, quickly grew up once more to woods, the edges first sprouting the tender growth of meadow grasses, shrubs, berry bushes and young trees that provide food for so many wild animals. The region not only became more heavily wooded than it had been, but it was now broken up into thousands of small parcels with abundant edge habitats, attractive to small and medium-sized herbivores.

With food and shelter restored, and with some protection afforded by hunting laws, many of the animals gradually returned. The proliferation of the white-tailed deer, once almost extinct in parts of New England from overhunting, was nothing short of spectacular. The resurgence of these animals was spurred by the absence of major predators. While the deer returned, the wolf did not. There was a job opening unfilled, a new predator niche waiting for an occupant. Add to the traditional predator fare a liberal sprinkling of garbage dumps, trash cans, backyard chickens and other man-made food sources, and the Northeast offered a new and unique environment —into which a new and unique animal, the Eastern coyote, moved. The long trek had ended, bringing the adaptable animal east via southern Canada and thence across the St. Lawrence into New York and New England.

Now that it is here, what are the chances that the Eastern coyote will survive? One consideration is public policy. The range of attitudes is suggested by two stories from Maine.

Early in the 1970s, camped in the deep woods along the Canadian border, biologist Daniel Hartman heard for the first time the unmistakable duet of two howling coyotes. "I was shaking, elated," he later wrote. "We have a new and noble predator in our state." In the fall of the following year, a deer hunter shot a 50-pound wolflike creature—apparently an Eastern coyote—and strung it up to public view in the pulp-mill town of Millinocket, Maine; scores of curiosity seekers drove in from miles around to see the rather pitiful-looking corpse.

Many of the visitors, John Cole of the *Maine Times* reported, did not share Hartman's respect: "Like primitive villagers gathered around the carcass of a man-eating tiger, they cursed, reviled and spat upon the dead coyote. Hanging gaunt and stiff, like a large gray dog, the animal hardly seemed awesome enough to warrant the group hatred it seemed to engender." Behind this performance, apparently, was both a deeply ingrained, almost atavistic fear of "varmints" and the assumption that the new critter was out to get the citizens' supply of deer, which constitute not only a major food source for many rural New Englanders, but help to boost local economies by bringing in hunters from out of state as well.

So far the Maine legislature, heeding the arguments of conservationists, has refused to put a "wolf" bounty on the Eastern coyote's head, although the animal may be shot at will at any time. Much the same situation prevails in other New England states and in New York, New Jersey and Pennsylvania. Massachusetts alone has reacted positively in the animal's behalf, by the simple expedient of not including him on the state's game list—any animal not specifically cited on the list is automatically protected from hunters. As one Massachusetts Fish and Game official puts it: "The Eastern coyote is an interesting animal and we'd like to be able to study him awhile."

The focal point of Massachusetts' study at the moment is the small, crowded Hampshire College office of Raymond Coppinger. A tall, spare outdoor type, Coppinger came to his research on the coyote by way of a general interest in

dogs. Over the past several years he has studied domestic dogs that have gone wild on the island of St. Kitts in the West Indies, before becoming intrigued with the wild dogs that he had heard reports of in Massachusetts and over the border into Vermont and New Hampshire to the north. In a pine grove behind his house, he also keeps a friendly, noisy pack of 40 sled dogs, crosses between Alaskan huskies and border collies, and when the snow flies he bundles them off in a specially built kennel-truck to compete in sledding events around the Northeast and Midwest.

PROPOSING A NOVEL THESIS

When Coppinger is not training, feeding or racing his dogs, he spends most of his time at Hampshire's modern, hilltop campus south of Amherst, planning his undergraduate course on wild canines and advising his students on their techniques in microscope analysis or running comparative skull measurements through a computer. One of the novel ideas Coppinger and his students are exploring is the thesis that wolves and coyotes, including the new race, may not be separate species but simply variations of one species divided into races or "ecotypes" that have adapted to different habitats by behavior and size. "All we really know," says Coppinger, "is that the New England canine is acting basically like a 45-pound animal, while coyotes act like 25-pound animals, and wolves like 85- or 100-pound animals. The original coyote is a small animal suited to the plains where it hunts alone or in pairs, surviving primarily on small mammals. The wolf, a much larger animal, needs far more food and gets it through a highly disciplined social pack that can surround, harass and bring down larger animals like caribou and moose. The Eastern coyote, intermediate in size between the two, is also intermediate in behavior. He is at heart an opportunist, a scrounger who can live on everything from berries to insects to garbage.

"He also runs in packs," Coppinger adds, "not big ones of 10 or 12 animals like the wolf, but small family groups that may include a friend or two but rarely add up to more than five or six. If necessary, this minipack can bring down an intermediate-sized prey like our small New England deer. Stomach analyses of road-killed and hunter-killed specimens, however, have yielded mainly skunk, raccoon or rodent hair, porcupine quills, feathers, apple cores, fowl bones and everything from scraps of leather to pieces of tinfoil and rope netting—the latter sure giveaways that the animal examined was stalking nothing more challenging than a family garbage pail.''

This resourceful opportunist is increasing in numbers, Coppinger and other biologists believe, although reported sightings indicate the population is still not very large. There are an estimated 500 coyotes in Vermont, fairly evenly distributed through the state; Maine has perhaps 500 to 1,000; Massachusetts somewhat fewer, found mainly from the big Quabbin Reservoir west through the Berkshires; and there are about 100 in Connecticut, almost all in the northwest corner of the state. From their experience with other animals, biologists believe that the numbers, whatever they are, will stabilize, and that when the new coyote race reaches an optimum growth in relation to available territory and food supply, a kind of built-in population sensor will go to work to limit reproduction, and any increase will stop.

With so few animals scattered over such a large area, research on the Eastern coyote remains difficult and much of the mystery about it is unresolved. Coppinger and his students will be out on snowshoes and skis again in the winter of 1975, trying to track their favorite animals and locate a den. It would help their studies greatly to have a few live pups to bring back and observe. The chase will not be an easy one, however, for the Eastern coyote, like the Western one, is cagey enough to dig several dens as insurance in case one is found. Such protection probably led to the failure of Coppinger's last search for coyote pups, during the early spring of 1974. Students had discovered fresh dirt and a hole near an old farm foundation, but despite every effort to sneak quietly away undetected, they returned after the whelping season only to find the den disappointingly bare. "Those animals are programmed to see us," says Coppinger with a not altogether grudging smile, "and not to have us see them."

Once rare in the Northeast, white-tailed deer, photographed near Massachusetts' Quabbin Reservoir, are joining coyotes in areas where farms have reverted to wilderness.

Enjoying a cool dip in a Maine pond, the moose is another beneficiary of the return of wilderness to the Northeast, which is now more forested than it has been for a century.

A stone wall that once bordered the fields of a New England farm is now surrounded by second-growth timber—a forest-edge environment that is ideal for deer and coyotes.

54

Mining Bonanza at Sea

GEOLOGISTS' THEORY POINTS TO LODES ON OCEAN FLOOR

by Tom Alexander

Early in 1974, a mysterious pair of ships began steaming in and out of West Coast and Hawaiian ports. Reports of the vessels' comings and goings were the chief topic of worried gossip among the international representatives meeting in Caracas, Venezuela, during the summer. They were there to try to divide up the world's ocean resources. For the "mysterious" ships are owned by a United States company, the Summa Corporation, and it belongs to the reclusive, incalculably wealthy industrialist, Howard Hughes. His men were at work testing the techniques and equipment for mining some of the deepest stretches of the Pacific Ocean. Summa is only one of a number of enterprises gearing up to go after the immense mineral riches that geologists only now realize lie at the bottom of the sea.

These companies are the vanguard of a new breed of mining prospectors who are shifting their sights from the land to the ocean depths in the search for scarce metals. Their first targets are millions upon millions of black objects the size of golf balls, called ferromanganese nodules, that lie on the surface of the seabed. The nodules contain, in varying concentrations, metals of greater or lesser value; and difficult though it will be to bring them to the surface, they promise to alleviate mankind's worries about the growing scarcity of many essential minerals.

Beyond the nodules lies a less accessible but even more tempting goal. For new scientific discoveries and insights suggest that not only is there unexpected treasure to be picked up from the seabed surface, but that the underlying ocean-bottom rock itself may contain rich lodes of metal. Discoveries about the seabed even cast light on prospects for mining on land; there is

Aptly named blackberry nodules, found in the eastern Pacific, are the seabed's richest in industrial metals such as nickel and copper. Those at left are around 100 million years old. The topmost nodule, three and one half inches in diameter, has formed around a central nucleus of basalt.

Fossil shark's teeth that litter the seabed are the most prevalent nuclei for nodule growth. Other "seeds" are shards of basalt rock spewed from subsea volcanoes. But some of the fastest-growing manganese encrustations form around a new kind of seed—tabs from pop-top cans.

Like a field of harvested potatoes, nodules crowd the Pacific Ocean floor. Miners look for densely clustered beds like this; scattered deposits are less economical to mine. Nodules are rarely found piled atop one another, nor are they found buried deep in the soft bottom sediment.

growing evidence that the oceans are the primary source of all of the world's ores, including those now buried under mountains and plains that lie hundreds of miles from the sea.

It appears, in fact, as though metals are accumulating on the seabed faster than man can consume them, revising the old view that minerals are nonrenewable resources. In one area of the ocean floor scientists have discovered that some metal ores may even have a biological origin—in other words, they are endlessly created by generations of tiny, one-celled organisms.

As explorers range ever more widely in the submarine world, many have come to believe that, acre for acre, the underwater two thirds of the planet is richer in minerals than the dry land. While this assumption remains to be verified, men have already found an abundance of undersea deposits, even though they have explored only less than 1 per cent of the ocean floors with comparatively crude techniques. Peter Rona, a geophysicist with the National Oceanic and Atmospheric Administration, compares present-day ocean-bottom prospecting to flying in a balloon, three to six miles up, in the dark of night, and trying to scrape up loose samples of rock with buckets lowered to earth on a rope. "How many mineral deposits on land would we have discovered this way?" asks Rona.

The ferromanganese nodules that stimulate such commercial excitement among miners have long intrigued scientists. They were discovered a century ago by the globe-traveling British oceanographic vessel H.M.S. *Challenger*, but remained curiosities until now. Reposing three to five miles deep in darkness, the nodules have been shrouded in controversy. It is now known that they grow slowly, accumulating mineral bulk from the sea—perhaps through the electrochemical action that attracts dissolved minerals in the water to the nodules.

And finally there are even some speculations that may explain why these nodules are almost always found sitting right on the surface of the sea floor—seldom even partly buried—despite a steady rain of sediment that has been drifting down on them for millions of years. "It's a real scientific paradox," says Dr. Robert Gerard of

Lamont-Doherty Geological Observatory. "These nodules grow only about one millimeter every million years, yet they somehow manage to stay right on top of sediment that accumulates at the rate of a millimeter every *thousand* years—a thousand times as fast."

Though nodules have been found to be widely distributed across the world's oceans, until recently they attracted little commercial attention, since most of them are composed mainly of manganese and iron, two metals mined more economically on land.

But in the late '50s, John L. Mero, then a graduate student at the University of California at Berkeley, found that certain nodules from the Pacific also contained substantial concentrations of copper, nickel, cobalt, molybdenum, vanadium and zinc that are worth a special effort to get. The largest and most promising deposits of valuable nodules that have since been found lie in a 150-mile-wide belt of Pacific waters north of and parallel to the equator. It begins off the coast of Mexico and passes south of Hawaii, ending in the vicinity of the Marshall Islands.

This belt (sometimes called the "Horn Zone" for the husband and wife team—David and Barbara Horn—who outlined it) is thickly carpeted throughout much of its extent with the sought-after "blackberry nodules," named for their dark, lumpy appearance. These have copper and nickel concentrations as high or higher than those in ores from many inland mine areas. They also have considerable cobalt, and some contain impressive amounts of metals in the rare platinum group—ruthenium, rhodium, paladium, cesium and indium, as well as platinum itself.

Mero estimates that the Pacific Ocean alone contains something like 1.6 trillion tons of nodules and that perhaps as much as 20 per cent are of commercial value. With an optimism and enthusiasm not always matched by other experts, Mero predicts that nodules should be so plentiful and so inexpensive to mine that they might some day put land mines out of business (and end the pollution and the landscape damage associated with them).

He also points out that nodules could ultimately defeat man's ancient enemy, rust, by lowering the cost of stainless steel. According to Mero, one reason that more manufactured items are not made from stainless steel is that nickel, a major component of the alloy, is relatively expensive. But Mero claims that nodule nickel could be obtained for a fifth of the cost of land-derived ores. It could therefore be economically feasible to fabricate all automobiles, bridges and even buildings of stainless steel. "Just imagine the iron and energy we could save if our automobiles didn't rust," he says.

In pursuit of such potential benefits, dozens of companies from at least half a dozen countries have been racing to perfect techniques for raising nodules from their resting places three to five miles down. Many different methods have been invented so far, including robot vehicles that crawl about the sea floor gathering nodules and then propel themselves to the surface.

RAISING NODULES FROM THE SEA FLOOR

In 1974, the most favored approaches were the hydraulic-lift and the continuous-line-bucket systems. Three American firms—Summa Corporation, Deepsea Ventures of Tenneco Corporation and Kennecott Copper Corporation—have all decided to use the hydraulic lift, which pumps nodules up to the surface through a large tube.

Deepsea Ventures' prototype apparatus consists of a submarine dredge that works like a vacuum cleaner and is connected to the mother ship by a large pipe. The dredge is towed over the bottom by the mother ship. To suck up the nodules, compressed air is pumped into the pipe at various levels. Because the air and water mixture in the pipe is lighter than the surrounding ocean, the inrush of the heavier sea water pulls the nodules from the dredge up the pipe. Deepsea Ventures has used a small-scale prototype to raise nodules from 3,000-foot depths in the Atlantic and expects a full-sized version to work in the 15,000- to 20,000-foot depths of the Pacific, where the copper- and nickel-rich nodules lie.

Summa Corporation's methods are hidden by the secrecy typical of a Howard Hughes venture. What *is* known is that the company owns two odd-looking ships built at great cost—$135 million according to at least one estimate. One of Sum-

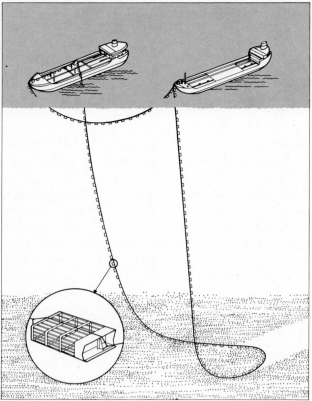

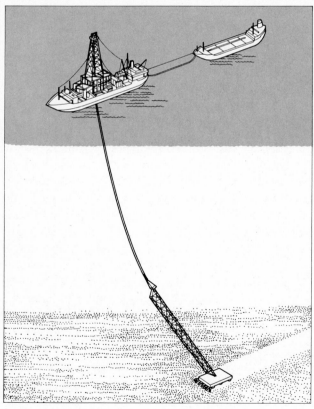

Mining with a continuous-line-bucket system (top), two ships carry a cable fitted with dredge buckets (inset) that scoop up nodules. The hydraulic-lift technique uses a pipe running from a ship to a dredge; pressure induced by air pumped into the pipe brings nodules to the surface.

ma's vessels, *Hughes Glomar Explorer,* is a mother ship that looks more or less like a conventional freighter, except that its superstructure consists of a strange, nonnautical jumble of towers and chutes, pipes and conveyors, along with a helicopter landing pad and other miscellaneous industrial appurtenances.

Explorer's companion vessel is even odder looking—a bulbous monstrosity of a barge that calls to mind a seagoing airplane hangar. The barge is completely submersible, and apparently contains a large, self-propelled dredging device that can crawl along the sea bottom.

In operation, the barge sinks below the *Explorer* and attaches itself temporarily to the hull of the mother ship; then, the sea-bottom crawler within the barge is connected to the electrical and hydraulic systems of *Explorer.* Finally, the crawler itself is lowered to the bottom, trailing three or more miles of 16-inch pipe and electrical cables that lead to the *Explorer.* As the crawler descends, the pipeline is assembled section by section aboard *Explorer,* with the help of the mother ship's towers, which resemble oil-well derricks. When the crawler-dredge reaches bottom, it pumps nodules up the pipe along with immense quantities of water. Both Summa's and Deepsea's dredges will be guided to and through nodule beds with the aid of television cameras.

The simpler continuous-line-bucket, or CLB, approach is the invention of a Japanese naval officer named Yoshio Masuda. CLB is being developed by some 25 different companies from several nations, all joined in a syndicate called the CLB group. The syndicate is headed by John Mero, the man who first noted that certain nodules were of more than passing commercial interest. Tests of a CLB prototype were carried out in the Pacific in 1972. Though mechanical troubles have brought the trials to a halt, they are expected—according to Mero—to be started again in 1975.

Potentially, at least, CLB offers a much cheaper solution to the problem of raising nodules than does the hydraulic system. It comprises nearly 10 miles of heavy, polypropylene plastic cable in the form of a continuous loop. Attached to this line, at 80-foot intervals, are hundreds of small dredge buckets, each capable of scooping up from one to five tons of nodules. The loop, held open between two ships slowly steaming parallel and half a mile apart, is lowered until it scrapes the bottom. Then, huge drums aboard the ships rotate the loop, dredging up nodules and dumping them into the ships' holds.

Although the hydraulic lift and CLB are seemingly simple in concept, both methods of harvesting are tricky—comparable to lowering a tube thin as a soda straw from the top of the Empire State Building in the dark of night to pick up grains of sand from the street. The possibilities for tangling and breaking or snagging of the equipment seem endless.

For all the problems posed by such methods, nodule miners using either technique can look forward to immense advantages. They are relieved of all the earth-removal tasks that land miners face. Seaborne miners also can transport their ores inexpensively by water rather than by truck and railroad. Nevertheless, gathering the nodules economically will take some doing. Since they are found only in a thin layer on the ocean bottom, a huge area must be swept to garner enough material to make mining worthwhile.

Presumably such obstacles will eventually be overcome by skilled engineers. For oceanographers—who have been studying the matter for more than 100 years—a far more perplexing question is how the nodules were created in the first place. Careful examination by these scientists of a large number of nodules is finally yielding some insight into how they are formed. When they are sliced open, nodules are seen to contain a central nucleus or "seed"—often a shark's tooth or a bit of basalt. The seed is surrounded by layers of growth rings, making it clear that nodules grow from the center outwards, like a pearl or a tree trunk.

One student of this growth process is Bill Siapno, who has specialized in the study of moon rocks brought back by the astronauts. In 1972 he made the switch from space to ocean and is now chief scientist for Deepsea Ventures. Instead of being perplexed by the formation of nodules, Siapno believes that their existence is almost inevitable, given the strange geological and electrochemical environment of the deep-ocean bed.

Siapno's laboratory is in the headquarters of Deepsea Ventures at Gloucester Point, Virginia. There, surrounded by nodules of every shape and description, Siapno ebulliently describes an undersea world more alien in many ways than the lunar surface that was his former specialty. He points out that the deep ocean is alive with electrical forces and fields totally unknown in the atmospheric world. In addition, sea water is full of dissolved metals and metal compounds in the form of ions—electrically charged atoms.

According to Siapno's theory, the undersea electrical influences steer the metal ions toward nodule seeds, on which the ions continually deposit themselves in an electrochemical process. "If there's as much electrical energy involved in the oceans as we have reason to believe," says Siapno, "then metals should plate out on a nucleus in the same way an automobile bumper gets chrome plated. This would occur on things like those fossil shark's teeth that we find almost everywhere. And it occurs very rapidly on anything made of metal. That's why we can find brass ammunition cases from World War II that already have a thin manganese encrustation. We even find a lot of pop-top can tabs on which manganese is accumulating, which will be helpful to us in dating nodules since we know the year pop-top cans were introduced."

NATURE'S UNDERWATER ELECTROPLATING

One of the results of Siapno's studies of nodule formation is his conclusion that the best way to refine the metal they contain might be to reverse the electrochemical process by which the nodule was formed—that is, if the process can be precisely enough established.

Siapno and some other scientists, like Gustaf Arrhenius of the Scripps Institution of Oceanography, also have a feasible chemical explanation for the mystery of why so few buried nodules are found. In the past, a variety of explanations have been offered for the peculiar ability of nodules to remain atop the accumulating sediment. These included ocean currents that roll the nodules around, and busy sea creatures that shove nodules up above the sediment. However, David

Fitted with a helipad and crammed with gear, Howard Hughes' 618-foot Glomar Explorer is the favorite in the race to mine nodules. The huge tower amidships probably aids in assembling the three miles of 16-inch pipe through which metal-bearing nodules are pumped to the surface.

A submersible barge works in support of Explorer in the Hughes sea-mining system. Dubbed HMB-1 (Hughes Mining Barge-1), the barge transports a bottom-crawling dredge too large to fit within the ship. Built like a floating dry dock, the barge is 324 feet long, 106 feet wide.

Horn who has taken thousands of photographs of deep nodule beds, reports that there are almost no marks in the soft sea bottom to indicate that nodules roll around; also, the photographs show few specimens of living animals except for an occasional flimsy brittle starfish or a sluggish sea cucumber—neither a creature strong enough to move a nodule above the sediment.

Siapno and Arrhenius have come to the conclusion that the existence of nodules depends upon a delicate chemical balance between an "oxidizing" environment, where plenty of oxygen is available to form indissoluble metal compounds, and a "reducing" environment, where acids and other chemicals act to steal away the oxygen. As it happens, this balance point often prevails at the seabed surface, the region where the sea water containing dissolved oxygen meets and reacts with the sediment containing acids born of the decaying organisms.

Because nodules are largely made of metal oxides, they can maintain their growth—and even their very existence—only in the presence of a plentiful oxygen supply. If anything happens to bury them in sediment, such as an undersea earthquake or a sea creature's fin-flip, the acids in the sediment go to work and extract oxygen from the nodule, reducing the metal into ions again. Then the ions percolate upward through the sediment and seek out new oxygen atoms

and another seed or another nodule on which to attach themselves.

The fact that the Horn Zone—and a few other spots—are the principal repositories of rich nodules is also being explained. Only these regions, it seems, combine the conditions of temperature, biological activity, depth, currents, sedimentation and undersea volcanic activity necessary to produce the chemistry that will result in the coveted blackberry nodules.

The Horn Zone virtually coincides with a narrow belt of bottom sediments consisting almost entirely of beautiful, intricately filigreed, microscopic spheres—the skeletons of tiny sea animals called *radiolaria*. This sediment, known as radiolarian ooze, is one of the most porous materials found on earth. And its properties play a part in an amazing phenomenon—the circulation of metallic ores through a biological process.

This biological concentration of some metals—mainly ores of copper and nickel—depends on the fact that iron and manganese oxides, such as those found in nodules, have a natural affinity for ions of copper and nickel. These latter two metals occur only as trace elements in ordinary sea water. On the other hand, certain biological organisms, including *radiolaria,* require traces of copper and nickel for their metabolic processes; in the process of growth, these creatures therefore perform as powerful concentrators of such

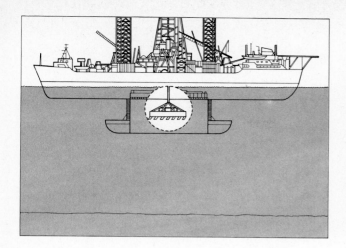

Though the company is secretive about details, the Hughes system probably operates in two stages as sketched here. The barge, carrying the dredge, is gradually flooded until it sinks and can be attached to the underside of Explorer. This first stage is accomplished in shallow water.

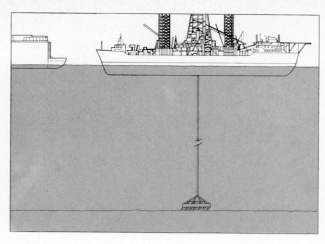

In the second stage, the barge transfers control of the dredge to Explorer, resurfaces and probably stays behind. When Explorer reaches the mining area, the ship lowers the dredge, which crawls through the nodule beds, steered remotely from the ship with the aid of TV cameras.

metals, which they extract from sea water.

When the organisms die, their bodies fall to the bottom as sediment. There the metals they contain are slowly released by the action of the acids in the seabed that result from decay. However, in the porous radiolarian ooze the metal ions of copper and nickel can work their way back up·to the surface of the sediment and attach themselves to nodules. Thus scientists can account for the phenomenon of inorganic metals having an origin in a biological organism.

Satisfying as this explanation is, it leaves open the enigma of how all these metals—rare and common—get into the waters in the first place and by what means the supply is renewed so that nodules can continue to grow. The answers to these mysteries seem to be emerging from the theory of sea-floor spreading, a concept that has been revolutionizing the earth sciences in recent years. *("The Wandering Continents," Nature/ Science Annual, 1970, pages 98-111).*

This theory envisages the entire earth as encased within a dozen or so thin, brittle plates that include both ocean bedrock and the continents. These plates are in constant, independent movement—a motion that is imperceptible, however, except to the most sensitive instruments. Moreover, the plates are also continuously being created and destroyed.

The creation occurs along a world-girdling chain of undersea ridges and rifts punctuated by submarine volcanoes. For reasons that are not entirely clear, lava from deep in the earth's interior, or mantle, comes welling up through these rifts and volcanoes. Chilled to brittleness on cold ocean floors, this lava becomes part of the surface plates on both sides of the rifts. These plates are constantly moving away from the rifts and across the ocean bed at the rate of one inch or more each year.

The destruction of the plates takes place thousands of miles away from the point of creation, in the vicinity of the ocean trenches, some as deep as 30,000 feet, that rim the Pacific Ocean. The sites of such trenches locate points where one plate has collided with another and overridden it. The overridden plate is deflected downward by the pressure of the upper plate and gets pushed into the earth's interior, or mantle. And over the course of millions of years, this deflected plate becomes reheated, melted and reabsorbed by the mantle where it originated.

The relationship of plate movement to the ongoing process of mineral formation has been suggested by several investigations in the Red Sea. There, at the site of a rift where the continent of Africa is being split off from the Arabian Peninsula, instruments lowered into certain deep Red Sea basins have revealed them to be filled by scalding water. When analyzed, the water

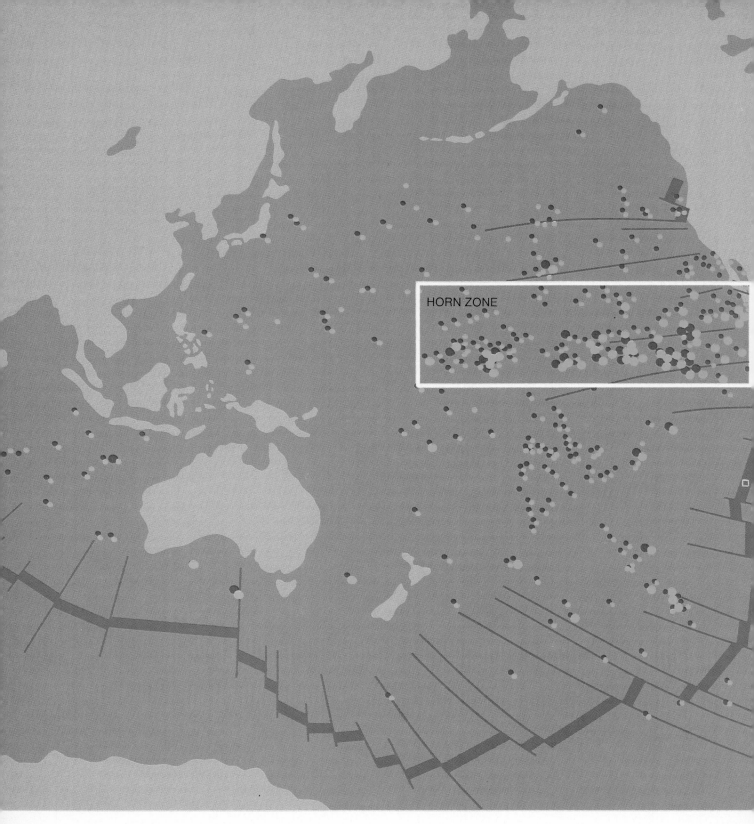

HORN ZONE

●● 1 to 2% copper   ●●●● less than 1% copper

●● 1 to 2% nickel   ●●●● less than 1% nickel

□ □ Hydrothermal Deposits

Midocean Ridges

The map above charts areas of the ocean bed where metal deposits—of two distinct kinds—have been discovered. More easily accessible for mining are manganese nodules, indicated by green and red dots, scattered across all the ocean bottoms, but concentrated principally in the Horn Zone of the Pacific. In this area, nodules are richest in concentrations of copper and nickel (color key). Less easily

mined than nodules are hydrothermal deposits (yellow) found on midocean ridges, where huge areas of earth crust, called plates, are continually forming and spreading out across the floor of the ocean through volcanic action. The difference between the two kinds of metal deposits lies in the way each is formed. The nodules are probably created through a chemical process set in motion by electrical forces in the sea water. Hydrothermal deposits, however, are formed when ocean water percolates through bottom rock, leaching out minerals as it penetrates into the earth's interior. There, subjected to intense heat and pressure, the mineral-rich water begins churning upward and finally regains the seabed surface through the rifts, where the dissolved minerals will precipitate out as sediment.

turns out to be a briny mixture—10 times richer in metallic salts than the sea above—made up of dissolved minerals including copper, gold, silver, iron, manganese, nickel, zinc and cadmium. Probing with coring drills, oceanographers have learned that sediments in the Red Sea basins are rich in muddy compounds of these same metals. At 1974 prices, the uppermost 30 feet of sediment in one Red Sea basin contains about $6 billion worth of copper and zinc alone, without counting the value of other metals in that stratum.

THE ORIGIN OF METALS

Scientists, pondering the origin of the metal-saturated sediment and metal deposits that are found near the midocean rifts of the sea floor, have offered the following explanation: As lava emerges from the rift, it cools rapidly, solidifies and fractures into fragments like those that occur when molten glass is rapidly chilled. Then sea water seeps down through these cracks and gets hot. Ordinary ocean water is rich in sulfur and chlorine compounds that act as powerful solvents, particularly under heat and pressure. As the sea water filters down through the lava, which has become fractured basalt rock, it dissolves traces of metal from the rock. Ultimately, these metal-rich solutions make their way into the region directly below the rift.

From that point, convection drives them upward—much as water surges through the central fountain in a coffee percolator. Approaching the sea bottom from below, these scalding solutions are cooled and relieved of some of their pressure. A likely result of these changes is that some of the dissolved metals immediately solidify to become veins of pure metal or metallic ore within the upper layers of rock. After the brines emerge through the sea floor itself and combine with oxygen in ordinary ocean water, the remaining metal forms muddy deposits of mineral-rich sediment like those in the Red Sea basins.

An American company, International Geomarine, was formed in 1966 to undertake the difficult task of pumping the Red Sea muds up from their resting place a mile and a half down. When the Arab-Israeli War broke out in 1967, the company was unable to get insurance coverage for its vessels; marine insurance firms feared that trigger-happy airmen from either side might take a crack at the miners working in their midst. International Geomarine has since sold its rights to the German mining concern Preussag AG, which is still working on techniques for lifting the muds and refining the metals.

Many geologists are convinced that rich as these upper muds are, they are probably only the icing on the cake. When the American Deep Sea Drilling Project's ship *Glomar Challenger* began deep drilling into the Red Sea floor in 1972, it encountered a hard layer of basalt rock just under the mud, it lost some of its drilling equipment and was unable to penetrate farther. But David Ross from the Woods Hole Oceanographic Institution in Massachusetts, one of the scientists in charge of that expedition, is eager to try again, for he believes that rich sulfide ores —and perhaps even pure silver—lie under the basalt. Small veins of copper have indeed occasionally turned up in cores drilled elsewhere by the *Glomar Challenger*.

Ross's belief springs in part from geological similarities between the Red Sea floor and the aboveground strata of the nearby island of Cyprus, one of the oldest and richest mining areas anywhere in the world. The copper, iron, zinc, gold and silver mines of the island were worked as early as Phoenician times, 4,000 years ago; in fact, the name Cyprus is derived from the Greek and Latin words for copper.

Cypriot mines continued to produce until, in the closing years of their empire, the Romans unaccountably halted their mining operations and sealed the entry tunnels. The mines were forgotten until 1912, when a young American mining engineer, D. A. Gunther, chanced upon an ancient account of them in The New York Public Library. Gunther went to Cyprus and after years of ingenious detective work finally found 10 old Roman tunnels, complete with intact support timbers and oil lamps. Since then, Cyprus has become one of the world's most important mining centers, as it was in ancient times.

Geologists believe that Cyprus is an old piece of sea floor that happened to get elevated above sea level when two plates collided and one of them buckled upward. In the millions of years since that happened, erosion has carved away capping layers of sediment and rock and exposed veins of ore. Thus, by implication at least, much of the present Red Sea floor can be expected to be just as rich in minerals as Cyprus.

Unlike those on Cyprus, most ore deposits found on land seem to be the product of a different process—but one that also ultimately depends on spreading of the ocean floor. The process develops in two basic stages. First, metals in solution are released from seabed rifts and are deposited on the ocean bottom nearby. The deposits are carried along by a moving plate that is thrust, as the result of collision with another plate, into a deep-sea trench and thence down into the earth's fiery interior, together with tremendous quantities of salt water. Over the course of millions of years, the metal-bearing sediments borne on the downthrust plate are heated and melted.

Then, the hydrothermal process goes to work once more melting and refining the metal compounds a second time. Again, the briny solutions percolate upward under great pressure, forcing their way through faults and crevices in the over-riding plate above *(drawing, page 65).* But this time they deposit their minerals as veins and ore bodies in volcanoes, such as those that form mountains parallel to the deep-ocean trenches.

Through the epochs of the earth's evolution, regions where plates have collided and formed deep trenches and mountains have been shifted inland by the accumulating growth of new continental land mass. Thus, the Ural Mountains, now some 3,500 miles from the Pacific and rich in valuable metals such as gold, lead, silver, copper, nickel, platinum and zinc, may represent the site of an ancient trench zone where, long ago —during an epoch of violent volcanism—the second stage of the double distillation process was carried out.

Though a good deal of work remains to be done to pin down the details of the process, it apparently sorts out different minerals into distinct bands lying side by side in predictable sequence —lead, zinc, copper, gold. This is probably mainly attributable to the varying melting tem-

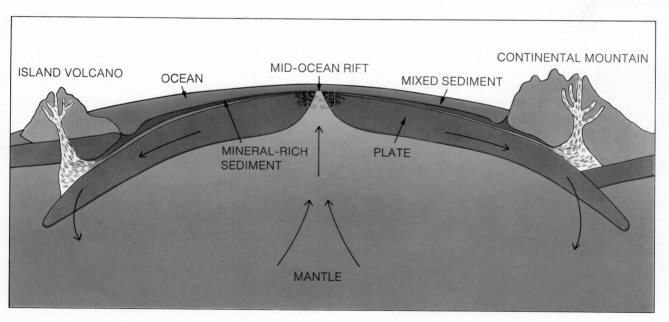

In the schematic drawing above, stages in the creation of metal deposits (green) are shown in relationship to a midocean ridge—with its rift opening—and to deep ocean trenches abutted by volcanoes. At center, sea water, which has seeped down into the mantle underlying the sea floor, dissolves metals from subsurface rock; then the water—pushed above the sea bottom by interior pressures—deposits the minerals on the plates that are spreading from the rift. As the two plates shown here descend into trenches, metal is redissolved underground, and migrates back up toward the surface of the earth—to be deposited there as ore bodies in volcanoes.

peratures of the different metals. Implicit in this fact is a potentially revolutionary improvement in mineral-prospecting procedures. The traditional method of searching was a hit-or-miss examination for surface outcrops of ore exposed by erosion. Most such outcrops have long since been found and exploited. But now, armed with this new theory of ore formation, metal prospectors may be able to select likely places to drill for subterranean deposits by looking for traces of volcanism where ancient plates have dived.

But, mining the seabed itself may offer long-term prospects for obtaining cheaper metals—a promise that is coming closer and closer to fulfillment. Unfortunately, this prospect, rather than being a cause of worldwide rejoicing, threatens to ruin the delicate international negotiations on laws to govern the uses of the seas and their floors. In 1970 the U.N. General Assembly declared that the deep-sea minerals were "the common heritage of mankind," and that profits from their extraction should be shared by all the peoples of the world.

A few of the underdeveloped countries that export minerals came to fear that nodule mining would lower the prices they might expect to get for their land-mined minerals and severely damage their economies. These fears have not been lessened by extravagant statements like that of nodule expert John Mero, who declares that "the initiation of production of most metals from nodules will, of course, signal the end of mining land deposits for certain metals." Ore-exporting countries that take Mero seriously would prefer to see no undersea mining at all. But if there is to be such mining, then they insist that the output should be tightly controlled by an international agency so that metal prices will not be affected once the nodules become an important factor.

Most of the richer nations agree that the benefits of mining the ocean ought to be shared worldwide. They are even willing to arrange special compensation for countries whose earnings from mineral exports may be affected. But they object to tight controls over mining and prices on the grounds that such restrictions would either discourage seabed mining or make the metals unduly, and uncompetitively, expensive.

The fight over these issues promises to be long and bitter. Because of all the uncertainty connected with undersea mining, most of the fledgling companies have been stymied in trying to raise the huge sums—estimated at around a quarter of a billion dollars plus for each full-scale nodule-mining and refining facility.

But one company is apparently undeterred by such problems. Howard Hughes and his staff are pressing ahead with their tests. Hughes calls his own signals. In the words of Paul Reeve, the general manager for Summa: "When we're ready to mine, we'll mine."

The lacy skeletons of one-celled sea animals called radiolaria may be the key to the formation of the metallic nodules found on the ocean floor. These creatures concentrate copper and nickel in their bodies and carry the metal compounds into sea-bottom sediment when they die. Later, the metal atoms work their way up through bottom ooze and collect on nodules forming at the seabed.

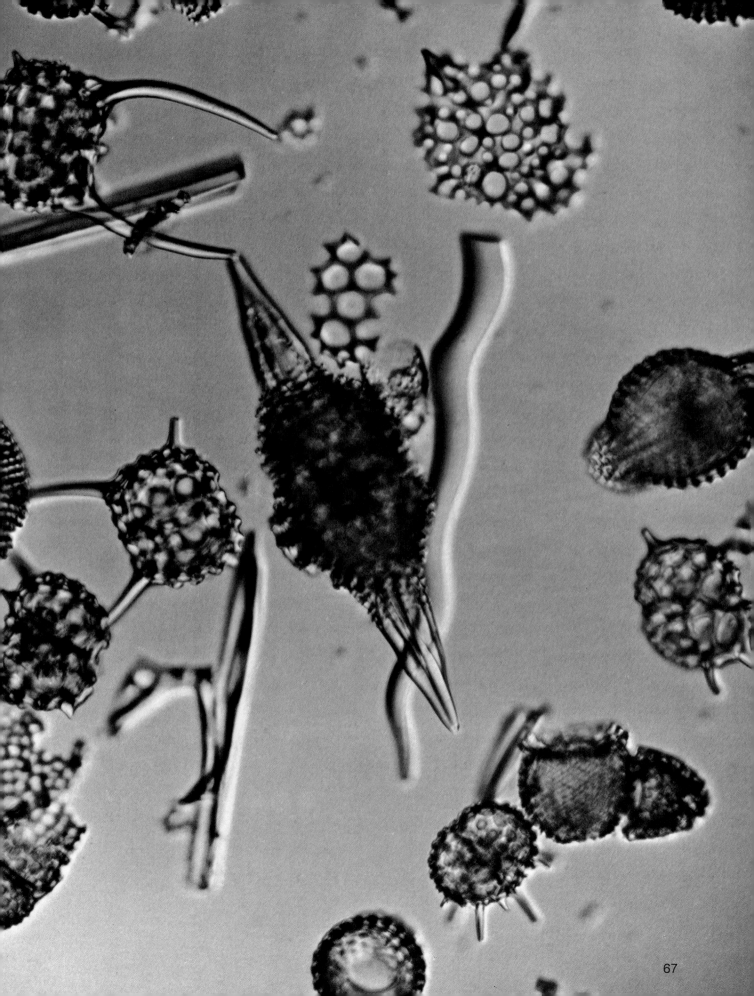

Parks to Save Himalayan Wilds

In Nepal, whose very name evokes an image of remote wilderness, two strikingly diverse national parks are taking their places among the most spectacular on the planet. One includes the earth's tallest mountain, Everest. The other, called Chitwan, is lowland jungle—only 200 feet above sea level—and contains two rarities of wild life: Indian tigers, remnants of a critically endangered species, and another species in great need of protection, the Indian rhinoceros.

In setting up the Mount Everest National Park in 1974, Nepal set a lofty example. Although the small kingdom lacked funds and expertise for the complex task, it took the view that the great mountain and its surroundings should be preserved as part of "a better world heritage." A handsome response soon came from New Zealand, whose Sir Edmund Hillary reached the summit of Everest in 1953. New Zealand offered to supply both financial and technical assistance and sent a team of experts, including Hillary, to Nepal to get the project under way.

One of about 250 Indian rhinoceroses in Chitwan displays its foot-long horn of keratin (the substance of hair). The horns are locally believed to have magical properties.

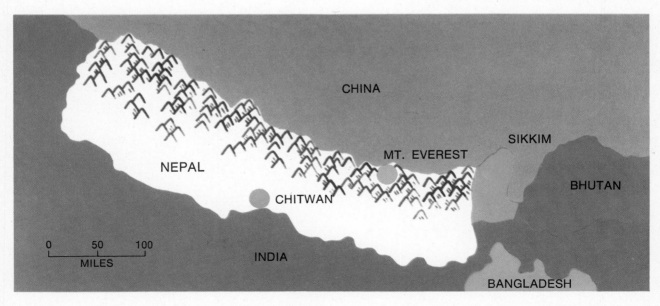

Chitwan (left) and Everest parks are less than 200 miles apart, but between them lies an ascent of 28,000 feet.

Jungle Touring by Elephant

When visitors arrive at the grass airstrip that serves Chitwan, they find an elephant taxi service waiting to carry them to Tiger Tops, a lodge built on stilts in the jungle. The elephants also provide transportation on trails in the park, enabling their passengers to come within camera range of leopards, wild boar, swamp deer, Himalayan bears, Indian bison, crocodiles, peacocks, pheasants and several hundred species of smaller tropical birds. With luck, visitors can also photograph tigers and Indian rhinoceroses.

The vegetation grows to enormous heights in damp areas, as at right, but elsewhere, it is sparse. The area had been over-grazed by sacred cattle, which destroyed food needed by large and small wild animals, but the establishment of the park has helped halt the damage.

Debarking at Chitwan National Park, tourists find no customary arrows reading "To Public Transportation." The transportation (left) merely waits, chewing grass.

An elephant taxi is almost lost in elephant grass, which grows up to 17 feet high. The howdah on the animal's back carries up to four passengers along the game trails.

Near the Narayani River, an Indian rhinoceros roots for food in the swampy reed beds where it spends most of its time.

Tracking the Lowland Animals

The first systematic studies of rhinos and tigers have already turned up some surprises. There are more rhinos than anyone believed—as many as 250 by a 1974 estimate—and they don't establish individual territories. The tigers are scarce, however, and do not move about much.

Rhinos are big and slow and easy to track. But tigers are nocturnal and, to follow their movements, scientists fit lightly drugged animals with collars carrying tiny radio transmitters.

An Indian tiger peers cautiously from elephant grass—a natural habitat that is being destroyed by villagers who cut it down to build huts.

The enormous environmental contrast between the two new parks in Nepal is recorded in this single photograph: the low-lying, flat

Chitwan area in the foreground and the mountainous five-mile-high Everest region on the horizon. 75

A Mountain's Delicate Balance

In establishing Mount Everest National Park, Nepal faced problems quite different from those at Chitwan. It was not large animals that required protection but the environment itself. In recent years there has been a steady increase in the number of visitors to the Khumbu Valley beneath the mountain—from only 20 in 1964 to 3,500 a decade later, enough to put great pressure on the delicately balanced life there. The Sherpas, who live at altitudes of 12,600 to 16,000 feet in the valley, are dependent on the thin forests for fuel. Each household requires at least one human load of wood a day. As more visitors enter the valley, more trees are cut to supply the outsiders with firewood and to provide fodder, in the form of lopped branches, to livestock herds. Fortunately the creation of the park came at a time when the damage could be halted and reversed. Visitors now carry their own kerosene heaters and cookers, and a reforestation program is planned to assure the Sherpas the timber and firewood they require.

Visitors to the area will not find an abundance of wild animals. Apparently there never have been many native mammals in the valley. But alpine plants and Himalayan birds are present in great variety, and above them loom the most spectacular visions to be seen in any park, the great white peaks that have lured adventurous men from the farthest reaches of the world.

A Sherpa woman carries her daily load of firewood along a mountain footpath, part of a network that constitutes the only transportation system in the region. Forests have been so depleted by the need for fuel that she may have to go 10 miles from home to collect the wood she needs.

The knife-edged peak of Ama Dablam, the killer mountain first climbed in 1961, reaches to 22,494 feet.

Brown and yellow rock lichens almost cover the gray rock. Common in the park, lichens are the only vegetation above 13,000 feet

Himalayan ground cover includes osbeckia (large leaves) and moss-sprinkled cotoneaster, which bears red berries.

Juniper grows at altitudes up to 12,500 feet, usually on southern slopes. Hanging from its branches is usnea lichen.

An immature griffon vulture, one of the more common of 100 to 125 species on Everest, scans the world below for prey. Full grown, its wingspan will be as much as nine feet.

Blood pheasants, usually in coveys of five to ten, are common in the area. As the seasons change, the birds move with the snow line, from about 10,500 to 14,000 feet.

Griffon vultures soar beneath an ice-clad peak. Overleaf, a Himalayan panorama shows the stark white summit of Everest at the left.

Furor over Brainwashing

A CURE FOR BAD HABITS RAISES FEARS OF MISUSE

by Gerald Jonas

B rainwashing is a dirty word. It implies an unwarranted intrusion into someone else's mind or the use of unfair methods to change someone else's behavior. A good many Americans associate brainwashing with totalitarian governments, like the Soviet Union and China, or with such grim tales of the future as George Orwell's *1984* and Anthony Burgess' *A Clockwork Orange.* But the psychological techniques of brainwashing are increasingly used in the United States, and fears of governmental misuse of them made front-page news in 1974.

The U.S. Bureau of Prisons was accused of trying to brainwash inmates of federal prisons. The immediate issue was a behavior-modification program called START (for Special Treatment and Rehabilitative Training), which had been in operation at the Medical Center for Federal Prisoners in Springfield, Missouri, since September 1972. START's mission was to turn uncooperative inmates into model prisoners using training methods originally devised in the laboratories of experimental psychologists. The prisoner shown opposite is going through a comparable "retraining" program at the Michigan Intensive Program Center, near Marquette.

The use of such behavioral methods in other settings, such as psychiatric clinics, has been hailed as a major advance in the treatment of the mentally ill. But START aroused opposition from the beginning. In this project, troublemakers from federal prisons were transferred to Springfield, put in solitary confinement for a minimum of one week and then allowed to work their way back to a "normal" prison environment by following a rigorous set of rules. The habits of obedience that the prisoners acquired were sup-

At the state-run Michigan Intensive Program Center, this prisoner is embarking on a six-stage behavior therapy program designed to reward improvement in conduct with such incentives as longer television-viewing hours.

posed to carry over to their behavior when they were returned to their former institutions. Instead, the prisoners rebelled. Several of the men assigned to START got word to the American Civil Liberties Union, which brought suit claiming that START violated the Constitutional prohibition against "cruel and unusual punishment." In February 1974, the government decided to close down the program.

It was the clearly involuntary nature of the START program that led to its cancellation. In the Michigan program, however, prisoners are not confined in solitary, nor are they penalized if they do not live up to their jailers' aims. Most important, each prisoner volunteers for the program and works out a contract with counselors to show that he understands the goals of the program and agrees to abide by its rules. Although the whole idea of behavior modification in prison has come in for increasing criticism, the Michigan program is still going strong.

Regardless of how such programs are structured, the methods used are all derived from a new and controversial science called behavior therapy. Behavior therapists believe that antisocial behavior—and most psychological problems—are the result of bad habits. As such, they can be best treated by breaking old habits and building new ones through systematic retraining.

For example, homosexuals who want heterosexual sex lives are divested of their homosexual desires after repeated electric shocks are administered as they watch pictures of male nudes. Children are toilet-trained in a few hours by therapists who coach them carefully—and award their progress with snacks. Alcoholics are turned off alcohol after taking drugs that produce nausea the moment they sip a drink, while phobias—from a fear of heights to a horror of cats—are cured by conditioning patients to accept the object or circumstances that trigger the phobia. Behavioral therapists feel their methods, which bypass the lengthy therapy sessions that are the mainstay of traditional psychoanalysis, not only bring quicker results, but surer cures.

These cures sound simple and direct enough. Indeed, generations of parents, teachers and employers have relied on similar schemes. Weekly

Injected with a drug that temporarily induces nausea when combined with any liquid, a problem drinker tries a sip of his favorite brew in "Duffy's Tavern" at Schick's Shadel Hospital in Seattle. After several repetitions, this treatment establishes a lasting aversion to alcoholic drink.

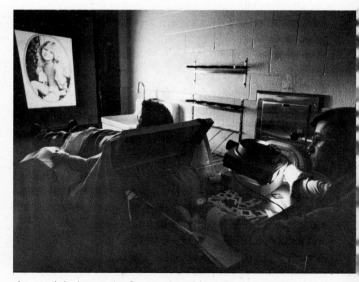

A sexual deviate at the Connecticut Correctional Institution at Somers watches a slide of a child. If he fails to say "Change it" within three seconds, a therapist may shock him through the electrode taped to his thigh, thus associating the shock with his abnormal sexual attitudes.

allowances, gold stars, merit raises are all ways of getting people to do the bidding of others. But behavior therapy goes well beyond these homely methods. It is a strict discipline, developed over the past 70 years, and is based primarily on the work of two men: a Russian physiologist and an American psychologist.

OLD DOGS: NEW TRICKS

The ground work was laid by the Russian physiologist, Ivan Pavlov. Around the turn of the century, Pavlov noticed that adult dogs salivate not only at the taste of food but also at the sight and smell of food. In a series of carefully controlled experiments, Pavlov showed that this kind of learning could be extended almost indefinitely. A hungry dog could be trained to salivate at virtually any stimulus (such as a ringing bell) that was repeatedly paired with the taste of food. After a while, the animal salivated when the bell was rung, even though no food was present. A new habit had been created. Furthermore, the new habit was reinforced whenever bell and food were again paired; such retraining ensured that the habit would persist for a long time. Pavlov spent nearly 40 years investigating the various factors that influence this process, which psychologists call conditioning.

Despite Pavlov's success in teaching old dogs new tricks, his method of conditioning was limited to a certain kind of behavior known as reflex. A reflex is an unconscious action that is automatically triggered by a specific stimulus, somewhat like pressing a button on a machine. Salivation is a reflex triggered by food. When salivation is brought under control of a new stimulus—such as a ringing bell—it is called a conditioned reflex.

Pavlov's work in conditioned reflexes with animals has an obvious application to human behavior, particularly in the area of emotional reactions, which, like reflexes, are often automatic and very difficult to alter by conscious effort. A fear of blood, for example, may be traceable to a painful childhood experience associated with the sight of blood. Once imprinted on the child's memory, the mere sight of blood may trigger his fear—just as the sound of a bell may trigger a dog's salivation. Pavlov's experiments with conditioned reflexes have shown behaviorists how many neurotic habits may be acquired through the accidental pairing of emotionally evocative events, and how such habits can be modified through systematic retraining.

In the development of modern behavior therapy, Pavlov's accomplishments in explaining habits based on reflex behavior were matched by the labors of B. F. Skinner, who investigated habits formed through trial-and-error learning. In his classic experiments with rats and pigeons in the 1930s and '40s, Skinner demonstrated how apparently spontaneous behavior can be brought under precise control by manipulating the immediate consequences of each act.

Skinner's basic technique was to wait for a hungry pigeon to make some kind of significant move, and then either reward it with the food or withhold the reward. The animal tended to repeat any behavior that was quickly followed by a reward, while unrewarded behavior faded away. Skinner called this method of controlling behavior "shaping." Thus, through a system of rewards and punishments, he could shape the pigeon into unpigeon-like behavior, causing it to peck at a lighted disc on the wall, or dance a figure 8. Above all, Skinner stressed the importance of breaking down a complicated task into comparatively easy steps, so that the performance of each step could be rewarded separately.

No one questions the validity of the Pavlovian and Skinnerian experiments. Problems do arise, though, from the application of experimental findings to human beings outside the laboratory. More specifically, controversies have sprung up from the distinction that must be made between behavior therapy in private clinics where patients volunteer for treatment, and prison programs, which are practiced on captive subjects whose options are obviously limited. Even if prisoners volunteer, they probably do so to have their sentences reduced, or to receive lighter work loads.

Perhaps the most notorious experiment in prison behavior therapy was conducted in the late 1960s at the Medical Facility of the California Department of Corrections in Vacaville. The experimental subjects were 64 prisoners who had repeatedly assaulted other inmates and guards; some of them had also tried to take their own lives. The experiment, based on a system that behavioral therapists call aversive treatment, using punishment rather than reward, depended on the threatened use of a drug called Anectine. Paralyzing all the voluntary muscles in the body and the respiratory system, Anectine produces feelings of suffocation and imminent death.

After being told about the terrifying effect of the drug—which wears off in a few minutes, leaving no physical damage—each prisoner was assured that he would get no injections as long as he avoided certain disruptive acts. These included stealing, trying to inflict injury on himself or someone else, deviant sexual practices and "unresponsiveness to group therapy." To show that they accepted these terms, all the subjects were asked to sign consent forms. Most did, but five who did not were added to the experiment anyway. Three had parental releases; two were included on the authority of the prison's Special Treatment Board, made up of four doctors, three of whom were psychiatrists.

During the year of the experiment, more than a fourth of the subjects received at least one shot of Anectine, and one got as many as six. The routine never varied; as each man lay helpless but wide awake under the influences of the drug, the prison doctor explained what the inmate had done to deserve the treatment and reminded him that future disobedience would bring the same results. Toward the end of the experiment the group seemed to become more cooperative. In a later evaluation of the statistical data, two researchers on the staff concluded that "aversive treatment is useful in reducing the amount of extreme acting-out behavior in male felons in a prison psychiatric setting."

Independent evaluations were not so enthusiastic. When word of the Anectine program at Vacaville reached the outside world in 1970, public indignation stopped further experimentation.

In theory at least, the START program at

A snarling German shepherd, projected from a slide, confronts victims of cynophobia, or fear of dogs, at New York's New School for Social Research. Patients see *a series of slides, progressively showing small, cuddly creatures, then larger dogs, and finally, lunging, hostile ones —until the phobia sufferers can touch live animals.*

Springfield, Missouri, was more humane than the Vacaville program because it relied on rewards, instead of punishments, to change behavior. The basic idea was to divide the program into eight levels, each of which would allow prisoners greater privileges than the one below. These privileges included more visitors, more showers per week, and so on. Good behavior was rewarded by a move to a higher level. But even at the top level, which could only be reached after seven months of virtually perfect obedience, life was no more comfortable than life in a typical federal prison. Moreover, these men were already veterans of solitary confinement and thus took pride in their ability to take whatever punishment the system could hand out without yielding an inch.

SITTING IT OUT IN SOLITARY

When transferred to START, some of these men chose to sit it out in solitary on Level I rather than cooperate with what they felt to be a degrading experiment. In an effort to force them to cooperate, the authorities apparently made conditions on Level I even less pleasant than the usual solitary confinement cell. An observer from the American Civil Liberties Union, investigating the prisoners' complaints, found some inmates shackled to their beds where, he was told, they had been kept for as long as four days.

Before the government decided to cancel START rather than defend it against the prisoners' lawsuits, a federal court in Missouri appointed a panel of three experts to evaluate the program. The court wanted to know whether START was soundly based in behavioral science, or whether it was simply old-fashioned prison discipline dressed up in pseudoscientific terms.

The panel was divided in its judgment. Two panelists, William DeRisi of the University of California at Los Angeles and Harold Cohen, then director of the Institute for Behavioral Research in Silver Spring, Maryland, found START scientifically misguided. They noted that even if the program achieved its goal of getting troublemakers to conform to prison regulations, it had not necessarily helped the prisoners prepare themselves for normal life outside prison. The third member of the panel was psychologist Nathan

Azrin of Southern Illinois University, who has earned a reputation for imaginative research in behavior therapy. He thought that START should be continued—especially since it seemed to be the only alternative for handling chronically uncooperative prisoners.

Azrin is by no means alone among behavioral scientists in giving approval to a program like START. In 1974, for example, the American Psychological Association—the largest professional society in the field—issued a statement asking the public not to confuse prison programs that use behavioral science for "clearly abhorrent" ends with other programs that are "humane, educational and effective."

One prison therapy program that seems to fit the APA's positive definition is being conducted at the Connecticut Correctional Institution, a maximum-security prison in Somers. The subjects are a small group of convicted pedophiliacs, men who sexually molest young children. Pedophiliacs are usually the first to condemn their own behavior as deviant, and other prisoners, even murderers, treat the inmates who have molested children as outcasts. According to Dominic Marino, chief of the mental hygiene unit at Somers, the aversive-conditioning program for pedophiliacs is completely voluntary. Each prisoner agrees to sit in a darkened room with an electrode taped to his thigh; when pictures of attractive children are projected on a screen, the subject gets an unpleasant shock —about six volts. Pictures of adults bring brief respites; the subject is informed that he can escape being shocked if he says "Change it!" as soon as a child's picture appears.

The goal of the treatment, Marino says, is to associate anxiety with sexual thoughts concerning children. Does the treatment actually work? Marino says that some subjects develop a completely different outlook on sex. One man described the change: "I start to fantasize [about children] but I can't go through with it. It doesn't make any sense to me anymore."

Marino is aware that his program is a dead-ringer for the brainwashing scene in *A Clockwork Orange,* in which the hero's sadistic urges are suppressed—along with his love of music and

Introducing twin boys to "wet" dolls that will serve as conditioning aids at the outset of toilet training, a Southern Illinois University behavioral therapist starts them on the course. By separating individual steps, therapists can toilet-train toddlers in as little as three hours—or at most, a day.

How Behaviorists Can Train Toddlers in Three Hours

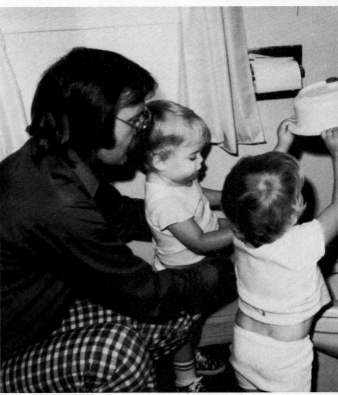

After using the potty, children are shown how to empty it into the toilet. They must also clean up any accidents.

After the doll wets in the potty, child and therapist pull up its pants and then offer it a potato chip as a reward.

The therapist helps a child dress following a successful use of the potty. At this stage, the dolls may be put aside.

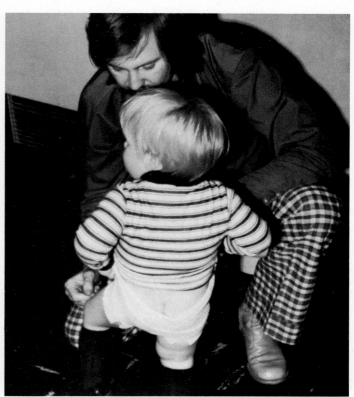

A little girl is asked if she is dry. If so, she gets a snack or drink. If not, she must make 10 practice trips to the potty.

Praising a toddler who has completed a training phase, the therapist offers her a glass of soda as a prize for dry pants.

everything else that stamps him as an individual. But Marino asserts that his subjects are not really being deprived of their free will, since they have already been enslaved by a compulsion they desperately want to get rid of; and that despite the implications of *A Clockwork Orange,* such therapy can alter negative behavior without destroying the rest of the personality.

Another prison program that apparently works, at least in some cases, is the Michigan Intensive Program Center—MIPC. Like START, MIPC is organized into levels (six in all), and prisoners move from level to level by earning points for good behavior. Unlike START, no prisoner is ever assigned to MIPC against his will. Each individual progresses at his own pace, and the program offers a real incentive for cooperation: educational opportunities far superior to those in most federal prisons. Many MIPC graduates who have returned to their former institutions are now pursuing college-level studies by correspondence. But it is not at all clear that a program like MIPC can have any lasting effect on the prisoners who pass through it. In May 1973, for example, a group of MIPC prisoners refused to return to their cells after a study session and had to be teargassed into submission.

Despite such failures, lawsuits and unfavorable publicity, the Bureau of Prisons has not given up on behavior modification. The Bureau is constructing a $13.5 million Federal Center for Correctional Research in Butner, North Carolina. There, by 1975, some 200 prisoners from other institutions will take part in studies of various techniques for modifying behavior.

As practiced outside prison walls, behavior therapy may use many of the same tools as the prison programs, including electric shock. But while there are appearances of authoritarian control, the success of the treatment actually depends on a close collaboration between therapist and patient. Both assume that the patient wants to get well. To do this, he tells himself that he will have to depend upon the therapist.

The use of behavior therapy to treat psychiatric problems came to the attention of the scientific community as early as the 1950s, when a South African psychiatrist, Joseph Wolpe, be-

gan applying it to the compulsive neuroses known as phobias. A phobia is a morbid, paralyzing fear of a certain object or situation. A person afflicted with a phobia lives in dread of touching or seeing or hearing about—or even thinking about—his particular nemesis. The list of phobias includes virtually everything: snakes, closed spaces, open spaces, high places, bats, cats, flowers, dirt, hair. If the patient's phobia is blood, the sight of a small wound (or even the thought of such a wound) may cause him to feel faint. The moment he looks away (or banishes all thoughts of blood from his mind), he starts to feel better. Each experience like this emphasizes the lesson that he must avoid anything to do with blood in the future.

In devising a behavioral treatment for phobias, Wolpe's approach was practical. Instead of viewing the phobia as a symptom of some deeply buried personality disturbance, Wolpe concentrated on the phobic reaction itself as a bad habit that could be erased, just as it had been formed.

FEAR OF BLOOD

One of Wolpe's early and most fascinating patients was a 23-year-old trolley-car driver who came to his office severely shaken because a few hours before a woman had walked into the path of his slowly moving trolley car. The woman had suffered only a superficial head injury, but there was a good deal of blood, and the sight had so unnerved the young driver that he was unable to go back to work. In a series of interviews with Wolpe, he revealed that his father had been killed in an accident 10 years earlier; ever since, he had been terrified by any glimpse of human blood, even his own.

At this point, a conventional psychoanalyst might have begun to explore the feelings of guilt or anger that the father's death had presumably triggered in the son—on the theory that once these feelings were exposed and dealt with, the phobia would fade away. But Wolpe was more interested in his patient's present reactions than in what had happened in the past. To weaken the link between blood and the phobic reaction it triggered, Wolpe had to get the young trolley driver to think about blood under conditions where he could not possibly become anxious. In this way, the patient could begin to build up a more normal reaction to blood that would compete with the phobia and then replace it. Wolpe hypnotized him, told him to relax as completely as possible, and asked him to visualize situations involving human blood, starting with a scene that would not cause feelings of anxiety and gradually working up to more provocative images.

STEP BY STEP TO STOP THE PHOBIA

According to Wolpe's account, the patient's first mental image was of "a slightly blood-tinged bandage lying in a basket." When he could visualize this without getting shaky, he moved on to contemplate the image of "a tiny drop of blood on his own face while shaving." Step by step, he worked up to a stage where he could think of "a casualty ward full of carnage and not be disturbed by it." After 10 sessions, he had overcome his phobia so well that when he witnessed a motorcycle accident in which a man was seriously injured, he was "absolutely unaffected" by the sight, and was even able to help load the blood-stained victim into an ambulance.

Although Wolpe originally asked his patients only to imagine phobic situations, many therapists now employ realistic props to make the scenes more vivid. In one recent Stanford University study, several patients who had a morbid fear of snakes were introduced to a harmless king snake by the therapist, who took them through a step-by-step routine that involved touching the snake's body, stroking it, holding it with gloved hands and finally holding it with bare hands. By the time they had worked their way through the entire sequence of steps, they were able, in the words of the Stanford report, to "hold the snake in their laps without assistance, to let the snake loose in the room and to retrieve it, and to let it crawl freely over their bodies."

Though phobias are the classic stuff of behavior therapy, behavioral scientists have made remarkable advances in recent years in treating a totally different kind of emotional problem. Nathan Azrin of Southern Illinois University has worked with 34 young children ranging in age from 20 to 36 months, who were having unusual

difficulty in learning to use the toilet. Amazingly, the children were toilet-trained in a few hours by therapists using a procedure devised by Azrin.

Most parents try to train their children by putting them on the toilet periodically and praising them effusively whenever they happen to use it correctly—or spanking them if they continue to have accidents. Azrin decided that what such children need is the kind of systematic training that a good athletic coach would provide.

Azrin broke the training task into a series of steps, and gave each child individual guidance and appropriate rewards at each step *(pages 90-91)*. If a child had trouble taking off his pants, the therapist took a firm grip on the child's hands and went through the motions with him. Since this kind of instruction involves a certain amount of physical restraint, the child also had a good incentive to learn to use the toilet by himself. Throughout the training session, any correct response to instruction was immediately rewarded with smiles, kisses, hugs, praise and the child's favorite foods. If the child had an accident, he was immediately scolded and made to change his pants and clean up after himself. During the final stage of training, the notion was planted in the child's mind that by staying dry he was pleasing the people he liked best.

Although the entire procedure may sound unpleasantly manipulative, the children apparently did not think so. Most of them, according to Azrin, enjoyed the few hours spent in the company of a friendly adult who gave them good things to eat and toys to play with, and who seemed genuinely interested in everything they said and did. Parents were equally pleased with the results. "The only parent who did not express pleasure," says Azrin, "had bet a friend $100 that his child would not be trained in a day."

While Azrin's success in potty training has demonstrated the scope and flexibility of behavior therapy, therapists have also been able to record progress in an area once considered the province of classical psychiatry: adult schizophrenia. One woman patient was admitted to a mental hospital because she refused to feed herself. For nine months, the nurses spoon-fed her. Then a behavioral psychologist noticed that the patient seemed to take pride in keeping her clothes clean. He told the nurses to begin spilling food on the woman's dress; the nurses, at the same time, were told to encourage any efforts on the woman's part to feed herself, and to praise her each time she did. After eight weeks of this simple reward-and-punishment regimen, the woman was eating normally; and a while later, she was able to leave the hospital.

The great promise of behavior therapy is that by ignoring causes and concentrating on symptoms, it can return disturbed people of all ages to happy, productive lives in a few days or weeks, rather than the months or years that conventional psychoanalysis demands. And significantly, the pioneering work of behaviorists like Wolpe and Azrin is being accepted by the medical profession. Even the prestigious American Psychiatric Association has urged psychiatrists to use the techniques of behavior therapy in treating their patients. For all the controversial fallout from the prison programs, such a seal of approval would hardly have been stamped on a system that could truly be called brainwashing.

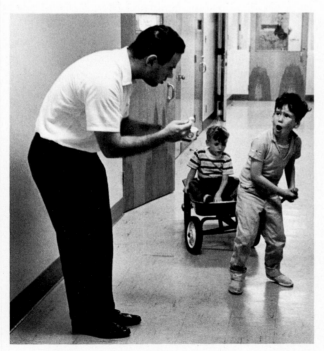

At UCLA's psychology department, which treats disturbed children—some suffering from inability to play with one another or to communicate with adults except in anger—a behavioral therapist listens to hostile back talk from Billy, who has been shown how to pull Chuck, a withdrawn fellow patient, in a wagon. Later, rewards of sherbet lure Billy and Chuck into an embrace—an early stage in a growing sense of communication with another human being.

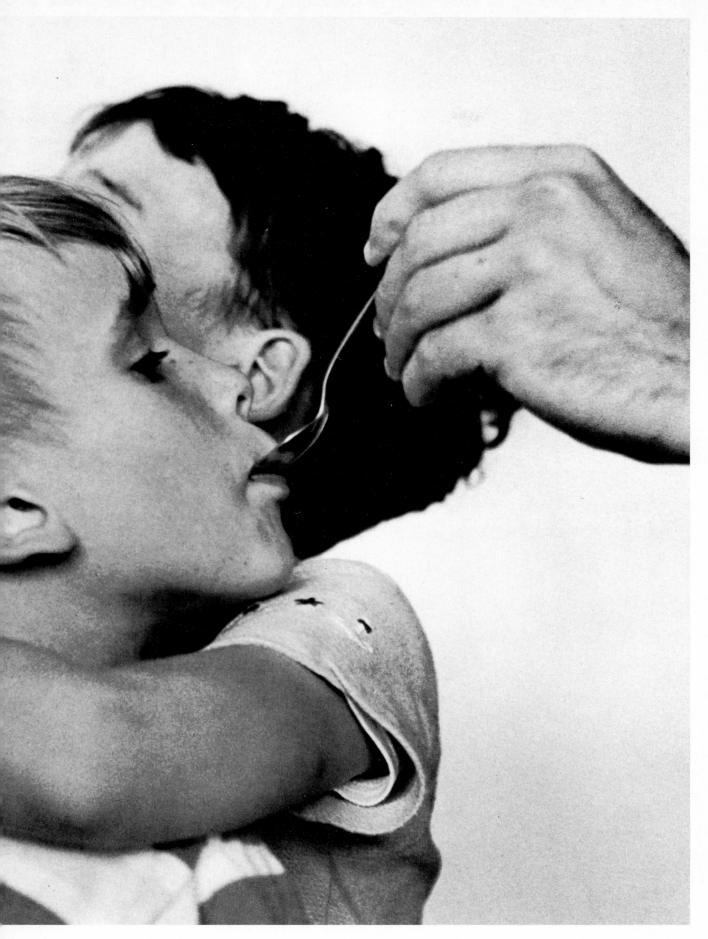

Domsat: Messenger in Space

In the thunder of rocket exhaust, three space vehicles were launched during 1974—two by private industry and one by the U.S. government —that were designed to provide the nation's first domestic satellite communications. Westars I and II, both owned by Western Union, were orbited in April and October, and ATS-6, an experimental government satellite, was launched in June. In 1974, other companies were pushing plans to field similar messengers in space; by 1976, RCA, AT&T and General Telephone and Telegraph will have their own communications vehicles in orbit *(pages 104-105).*

International communications satellites have long been transmitting special interest programs —such as World Cup soccer matches and the 1973 wedding of Britain's Princess Anne—between continents. But the new U.S. satellites, called domsats, should meet a long-felt need for a domestic communications system capable of transmitting transcontinental telephone calls, television and radio programs and facsimiles of printed and graphic matter, as well as linking scattered business offices to a central computer.

Unlike the company-owned satellites, ATS-6 was designed solely as a prototype for future generations of domsats and thus is larger, more complex and some 50 times more powerful than the Westars. ATS-6 has already demonstrated its potential by beaming TV programs and two-way medical consultations to 119 ground stations serving remote American communities.

Whether operated by government or industry, the satellites' costs to users will eventually be lower than those of ground-based communications systems; such systems require scores of expensive towers to relay information over great distances, since the microwave beams they use have a practical range of only about 50 miles. By contrast, a domsat, orbited some 22,300 miles high, will be able to beam to huge chunks of the earth's surface without auxiliary towers.

In 1910, uniformed Western Union boys like this messenger rode bicycles to hand-deliver telegrams. In 1974, the company began relaying some of its messages by satellite.

Lifting from its launch platform at Cape Canaveral, a Delta rocket carries the first U.S. domestic communications satellite into a circular orbit high over the Pacific Ocean.

96

Anchored to its testing cradle, Westar I is just about to be lifted into a thermovacuum chamber that simulates the conditions in deep space.

Torturous Tests That Mimic Outer Space

Long before Westar was launched, technicians at Hughes Aircraft Company's California plant put it through its paces on the ground. The tests copied space conditions so exactly that after 18 months the Hughes experts were sure that the messenger satellite would perform perfectly during its estimated seven-year lifetime. To determine how the Westar systems would function under extremes of heat and cold, the satellite was tested for 120 hours in the thermovacuum chamber at left. The walls of the chamber were chilled to —300° F. by liquid nitrogen to simulate the cold of space, and powerful lights in the chamber's top simulated the effects of the sun.

The most painstaking tests were conducted on the domsat's antispin motor, which acts to counter the satellite's spin in space, and keeps its antenna assembly stationary and pointed toward the earth. The motor was subjected to nine vibration tests and was kept running the entire time the satellite was in the thermovacuum chamber. The most essential Westar component could not be test fired at all. The solid-fuel motor that boosts Westar into a proper orbit can only be fired once, and that of course is in space. To compensate, technicians ignited a duplicate in a steel-lined airless chamber—a close copy of the conditions it later encountered in orbit.

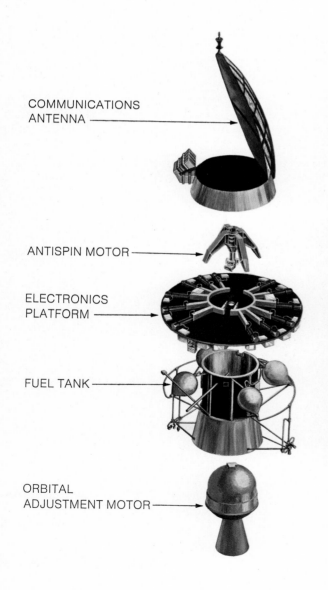

COMMUNICATIONS ANTENNA

ANTISPIN MOTOR

ELECTRONICS PLATFORM

FUEL TANK

ORBITAL ADJUSTMENT MOTOR

A technician (foreground) tests a Westar electronics array, while a second works on a satellite's antenna. At left is an exploded view of the Westar-type satellite, including the antenna, which transmits television, telephone and facsimile signals to earth, an electronics platform, which amplifies the signals and a motor that positions the satellite in orbit.

Visiting the Doctor by Satellite

In the past year, ATS-6, with its enormous beaming power, has been reaching out beyond the normal range of TV stations—but not with the ordinary programing. The government satellite transmits special services such as a two-way hookup that allows patients to consult physicians and specialists scores of miles distant.

For example, ailing residents of Galena, Alaska were connected with doctors in a receiving station near Fairbanks, 260 miles away. Linked to the station via ATS, the patients were able to talk with the doctors while they were examined by paramedical attendants in Galena. If a patient needed further assistance, specialists could be consulted in Anchorage, 325 miles away.

Incongruous in a remote Alaskan settlement, this space-age antenna is connected to one of 119 ground stations that receive television and radio broadcasts relayed by ATS-6.

Dwarfing the technicians beneath it, the giant ATS-6 satellite displays the extra-large umbrella antenna that enables it to transmit to remote areas of the U.S.

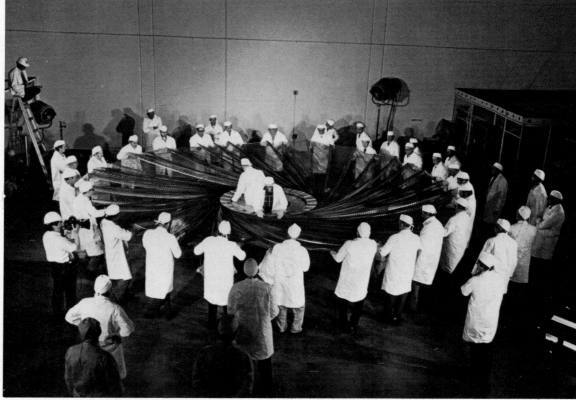

Like priests in a ritual dance, white-clad technicians solemnly fold the spiral arms of the ATS-6's antenna after test

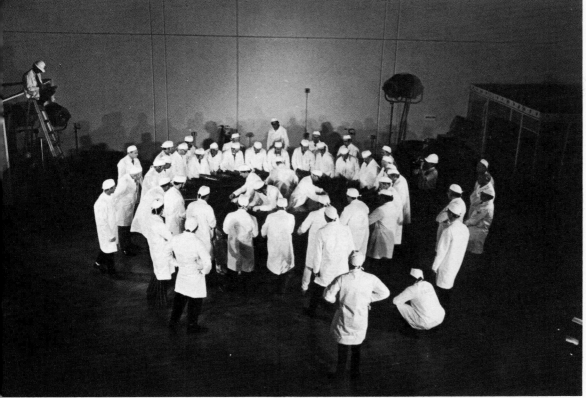

ability to open in space. Since there is no mechanism to close the antenna, it must be shut by hand.

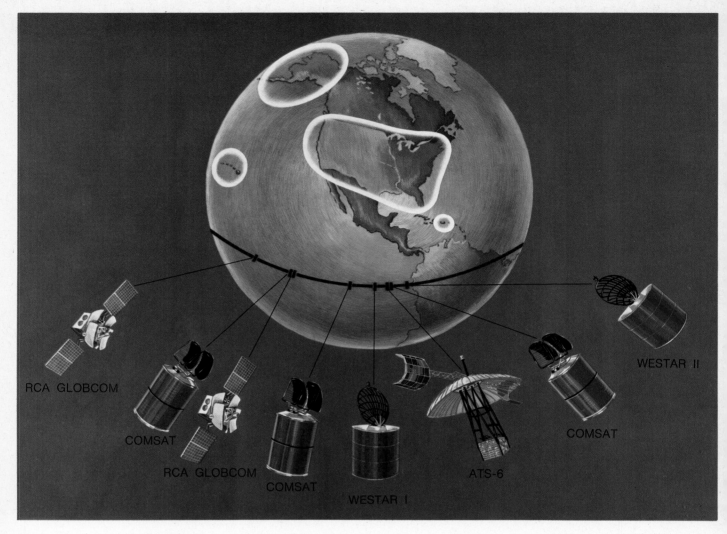

Displayed over the territories they will serve, these domsats will provide satellite communications for the entire U.S. by the end of 1976.

RCA GLOBCOM

COMSAT

RCA GLOBCOM

COMSAT

WESTAR I

ATS-6

COMSAT

WESTAR II

Tough Competition for the Best Orbits

By late 1976, ATS-6 and the Westars will be joined in orbit by five other domsats: three Comsats operated by AT&T and General Telephone and Telegraph, and two Globcoms owned by RCA. But because there is only one area—in a band over the Pacific west of the Galápagos Islands—from which a satellite can reach all 50 states, the domsats will be competing fiercely for the most desirable space.

A satellite stationed outside this window loses some of its ability to reach the whole country with clear signals. But because signals might become garbled if the satellites are clustered too close together, only three can orbit in the prime area at once. Thus, the companies have been lobbying with the Federal Communications Commission, the agency that will allocate domsats' space. The stakes are high. A space messenger situated in the window would be highly competitive with other satellites; through the lease of its telephone circuits, its owner could in fact expect to earn an additional $130 million a year.

No matter which group of domsats wins this battle for space, the real benefits will go to consumers. Future domsats may even be able to beam films direct to theaters—lowering distribution costs and helping to reduce the price of a ticket to the movies.

The antenna of Earth Station I in northern New Jersey is trained at Westar I. ES-I also controls four other satellite transmitting stations.

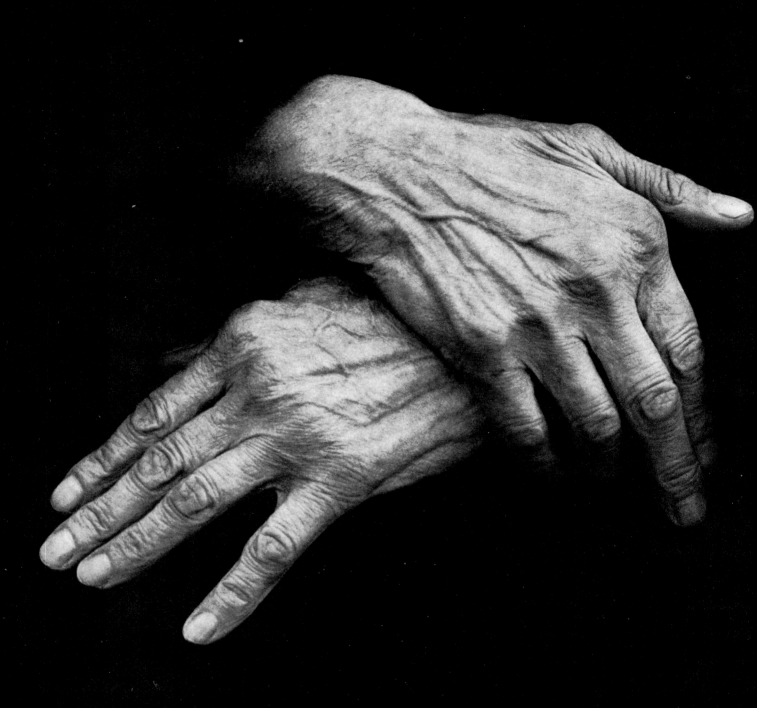

The Death of Old Age?

RESEARCHERS CLOSE IN ON THE BODY'S CLOCK OF AGING

by Albert Rosenfeld

Most people think of growing old as a regrettable but inevitable consequence of life. For the first time in history, this assumption is being challenged by a group of responsible scientists. Of course, there has never been any shortage of quacks eager to capitalize on the human desire to stay young and to live longer; in the early 1900s charlatans were touting yoghurt as a youth potion, and in the 1920s they were selling monkey gonads to unwise old men. But only in the last few years has widely accepted research raised a serious possibility of winning the fight against old age.

For a long time, the study of the aging process languished in the shadow of triumphs of curative medicine. These victories over the debilitating infirmities of advancing years have ranged from the use of bifocals for age-weakened eyes to the implantation of pacemakers for age-weakened hearts. But such advances got at symptoms, not causes. They could never promise more than a series of holding actions in an ultimately losing battle. Today, however, among those who might be called the avant-garde of gerontology, there are several investigators who are almost evangelically optimistic about their chances of learning how to slow down, and possibly even reverse, the aging process.

These new gerontologists pin their hopes on a large and diverse body of evidence that seems to point to one conclusion: The cause of aging is not outside us, but within us. People do not simply wear out under an incessant rain of hard knocks from the environment, as many conservative experts still believe; rather, all living creatures carry around within themselves a precisely timed self-destruct mechanism, a clock of

Eroded by time and the body's chemistry, the hands of an 82-year-old woman reveal the deterioration that may be slowed by finding—and resetting—a built-in clock of aging.

aging that ticks away vitality and ensures that no individual of any kind will significantly outlive other members of its species.

At first glance, such a conclusion may seem to be more of a warrant for pessimism than for optimism. But researchers like Bernard Strehler of the University of Southern California and W. Donner Denckla of the Roche Institute of Molecular Biology in Nutley, New Jersey, point out that if aging is really controlled from within, it should be possible to identify the mechanism, discover how it works and perhaps find a way to counteract it. Strehler and Denckla disagree on where inside the organism the clock of aging is most likely to be found, but both believe a breakthrough may be close at hand. Strehler, one of the most impatient of the new gerontologists, goes so far as to predict: "The aging puzzle could be essentially solved by the year 2000."

Among the more recent developments that seem to support such optimism:
• Experiments show that many creatures live longer if their body temperatures are lowered a few degrees by keeping them constantly in cool surroundings, or if they are fed a very low-calorie diet. Among the 1974 discoveries was a new drug that lowers body temperature, apparently by turning off the brain's thermostat.
• Another drug has been found to help the body get rid of metabolic waste products that tend to build up, like uncollected garbage, in aging cells; this same drug has been used in France to alleviate the symptoms of senility.
• Cells taken from human embryos and maintained in laboratory cultures more than doubled their expected life span after being dosed with tocopherol, better known as vitamin E.
• With the aid of a new laboratory technique, a leading American gerontologist has tracked the cause of aging directly to what he considers its lair—in the genetic storehouse of the nucleus of each individual cell.

Perhaps even more significant to the long-run conquest of aging was one 1974 development that took place not in a laboratory but in the halls of Congress: A bill was passed creating a new National Institute on Aging, to oversee research efforts and coordinate the activities of other agencies working in the field. This action, at a time when so many areas of science are competing for limited research funds, gives aging research a mark of prestige that virtually guarantees a high level of public and private support for major projects.

The magnitude of the task facing the Strehlers and the Dencklas can best be appreciated by recalling the life span allotted to man in the Bible. The 90th Psalm warns that, "The days of our years are threescore years and ten; and if by reason of strength they be fourscore years, yet is their strength labour and sorrow; for it is soon cut off, and we fly away." And a verse in the Book of Isaiah looks forward to a bright future when no man will die before his time, which is clearly stated to be 100 years.

IS 100 YEARS THE UPPER LIMIT?

These figures might have been taken from the actuarial tables of a 20th Century insurance company. About 100 years remains the upper limit for most humans—despite the tales, now challenged, of long-lived communities in remote mountain areas *(pages 110-111)*. Once a person turns 70, the odds that he will survive to his next birthday still drop sharply. The change is only in the number of people who make it to 70 or 100.

In conquering many of the diseases and cleaning up many of the unsanitary conditions that used to kill off people prematurely, science has made it possible for more and more people to live out their Biblical life spans. Very few people in ancient Palestine reached their 70th birthday, whereas living for 70 years is a normal occurrence today. But a 70-year-old patriarch in the First Century A.D. had as many years left to live as does a 70-year-old American in 1975—even more, probably, since the patriarch had to be so much tougher than the American to reach the age of 70 in the first place.

These facts may sound incredible to anyone who is familiar with the modern medical arsenal of miracle drugs and life-sustaining machines. But what the medical sciences have accomplished in extending the average life expectancy is the equivalent of removing most of the obstacles in a hurdle race so that more contestants

Held by a scientist, the age-slackened aorta of a 62-year-old man is larger than the one at left, from a younger man.

The healthy wall of a 20-year-old aorta includes an outer blue layer of nerves, connective tissue and blood vessels at top, a purple layer of muscle, and a thin blue inner layer of lining tissue. Brown gel supports the aorta walls.

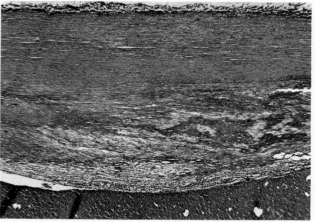

In the 62-year-old aorta, above, the blue inner layer of lining tissue is greatly enlarged and riddled with fatty deposits. This clogging, atherosclerosis, constricts the flow of blood and is a common disease of old people.

Debunking the Modern Methuselahs

Until his recent death, reportedly at the age of 168, Shirali Muslimov enjoyed the honor of being the oldest citizen of the Soviet Union and perhaps the world. A native of the Caucasus Mountains, a region that has long been famous for its extraordinary number of supercentenarians, Muslimov was examined by gerontologists and photographed for newspapers and magazines. Despite Muslimov's notoriety, the actuality of his and other Methuselahs' years has now been challenged.

In 1974, Zhores A. Medvedev, an eminent and outspoken Soviet biologist working in exile in London, debunked such claims of extreme old age. Medvedev wrote in the British magazine, *Gerontologist,* "The trouble is that many scientists have taken for granted that these old people are telling the truth." Not one of the 500 or so people in the Caucasus region who is supposedly 120 or more years old has been able to produce reliable birth records. (Official birth certificates, after all, are a fairly recent invention.) Furthermore, medical tests indicate that the bodily functions of these old people are about the same as those of a 60-year-old.

The exaggeration of age is ascribed by Medvedev to politics, tradition—and draft dodging. In the Caucasus and elsewhere, he writes, "the most elderly people are regarded almost as saints." Politics certainly played a part when the supposed longevity of people in the Caucasus was promoted by native son Stalin; his interest in the legend increased with his own years and prompted local authorities to find more and more cases to prove the belief.

Another explanation for extreme longevity, says Medvedev, is that large numbers of draft dodgers and deserters from World War I avoided detection by exaggerating their ages with their fathers' papers. The same practice probably was common during World War II, and Medvedev wryly predicts a boom in patriarchs as this crop of pseudo-ancients ages further.

Shirali Muslimov was reputedly 168 years old when he enjoyed a gallop in the Caucasus. At this remarkable age he also tended the orchard he planted in the 1870s.

Enjoying a pensive smoke on her front porch, Khfaf Lasuria (right), a native of Soviet Georgia, claims to be 141 years old. She has just recently retired from her job as a tea picker.

The effects of aging have been compared to repeated copying of a photograph (above and right), since the body mechanisms require repeated reproduction of molecules.

After five copyings, the photograph is barely recognizable. Similar degradation in regeneration of tissues has been blamed for the accumulating deterioration with age.

can reach the finish line. As impressive as this achievement may be, it is not the same as extending the maximum life span, which would require pushing back the finish line itself.

Many scientists—perhaps even the majority —remain skeptical that the finish line can ever be pushed back. To them, aging is a cumulative process of wear and tear that cannot be arrested, any more than the erosion of a sand beach by a pounding surf can be arrested. Under the stresses and strains of daily life, the body begins to fall apart. Deterioration takes a great many forms; the wrinkle and sag of skin, the dimming and dulling of eye and ear, the gradual decline in efficiency of lungs, heart, liver, kidneys, arteries and brain. Individual cells dry out. Connective tissue gets tough and fibrous. The whole organism loses substance; it shrinks. And in its weakened state, it is more susceptible to serious infections, cancer, arthritis, heart disease, diabetes and senility.

To other, more venturesome experts, however, the very inevitability of the scenario argues against the wear-and-tear hypothesis. If aging is due primarily to wear and tear, then why doesn't an occasional very strong or very careful individual live to a vigorous 140 or 150? And, even more significantly, why is the variation in life span from species to species so much greater than the variation between individuals within any given species? A mouse is ancient at three years, a horse at 30, a man at 100, but a Galápagos tortoise may still be going strong at the age of 150. These facts—and much other evidence—suggest that every individual in every species dies in accord with a predetermined schedule. The question is, what determines the schedule?

Among a great many differing answers to that question, two principal lines of thought can be discerned. Most members of the gerontological avant-garde believe that the clock of aging must lie inside the individual cell. Bernard Strehler, a principal exponent of this belief, assumes that the body dies because its individual cells wear out and die, and so his research is focused on the core of genetic material that controls the behavior of every cell from within.

Other experts, such as Donner Denckla, believe the clock lies not within every cell, but in certain hormone-triggering brain cells, which set off an aging process that affects the rest of the body. Denckla is searching for one or more substances that he calls death hormones—substances that, once released into the bloodstream, can orchestrate the decline and demise of all the body's 60 trillion variegated cells.

THE LIFE OF THE CELL

At the moment, it is impossible to say which theory, if either, will turn out to be right. But if there is a cellular clock of aging anywhere in the body, the mechanism is likely to involve the cell's packet of DNA—the long, precisely coiled molecule that constitutes a manual of genetic instructions and tells the cell exactly what to do. Among these instructions are some that are thought to regulate the life span of the cell.

Even in the same body, some cells live longer than other cells. In many kinds of tissue—the skin and gut lining, for example—a certain percentage of cells is always dying off while others are dividing so as to give birth to new cells. A typical cell in the intestine lining lives for only about a day and a half before it dies and is replaced. But other cells, such as those in the heart and the nervous system, sooner or later lose their capacity to divide although they can live as long as 100 years or more. Yet many nerve cells never get to live out their potential life spans. After the age of 35, for instance, the average person loses 100,000 brain cells every day.

Obviously, there is something very basic at work here—something that not only interferes with the DNA's control of cell operations but does so in a way that cannot be corrected by the cell's repair mechanism. The most logical place to look for such a disturbing factor is in the master control, the DNA molecule itself. In a cell that can reproduce, the DNA might fail in the crucial job of making duplicates of itself for new cells, and the offspring DNA could be subtly different from its parent molecule, changing cell control in a way that causes deterioration.

This deterioration is compared by England's Alex Comfort, one of the world's leading gerontologists (and author of The Joy of Sex), to what happens when photographs are reproduced. "If we make a negative by photographing a photograph, then print that negative and photograph the new photograph and so on, the successive copies will be of lower and lower quality," Comfort says. "Similarly, successive generations of dividing cells may become less and less effective, so that the new cells produced by an old man are in some ways less viable than the new cells that he produced when he was a child." The genetic control might also be damaged by the random impact of cosmic rays tearing through the cell—a theory proposed by the late Leo Szilard, the noted atomic physicist.

According to other theorists, errors might creep into cell operations regulated by DNA even if the DNA molecule remains intact, and such a failure would affect both dividing cells like blood cells and nondividing ones like brain cells. The DNA manages the cell's production of protein, the stuff of living tissue, by directing the work of its principal assistants, the RNA molecules, in conjunction with chemicals known as enzymes. Damage that harmed a critical RNA molecule or an enzyme could, in effect, knock out an assembly line worker who was uniquely qualified to do a particular job. Components might come off the line improperly put together; production might grind to a halt if defective parts piled up faster than the cell was able to get rid of them. The result could be a rapid escalation toward what Leslie Orgel of the Salk Institute has called an error catastrophe.

One system that might easily be crippled by an error catastrophe is the immune system, which defends the body against invading microorganisms and other foreign matter. In order to function properly, the cells of the immune system must be able to distinguish friend from foe or, as the immunologists put it, self from not-self. But with increasing age, the immune system often begins to attack some of the body's own cells.

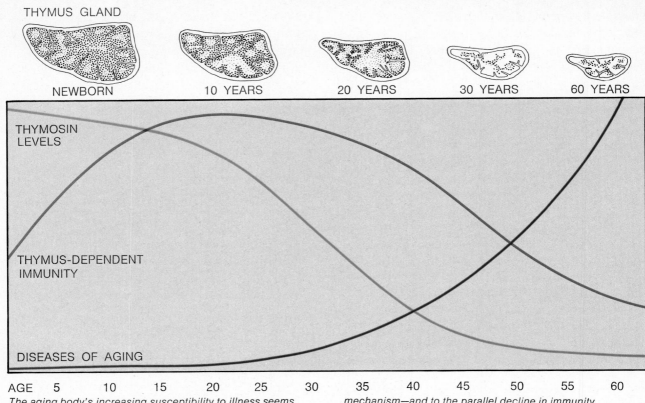

THYMUS GLAND

NEWBORN   10 YEARS   20 YEARS   30 YEARS   60 YEARS

THYMOSIN LEVELS

THYMUS-DEPENDENT IMMUNITY

DISEASES OF AGING

AGE   5   10   15   20   25   30   35   40   45   50   55   60

The aging body's increasing susceptibility to illness seems to be directly related to declining levels of thymosin— a hormone controlling part of the body's disease-fighting mechanism—and to the parallel decline in immunity conferred by thymosin. At the same time the thymosin-producing thymus gland shrinks steadily with age.

This dreadful mistake may come about because of flaws in the immune cells or because the cells being attacked have undergone changes that make them "look foreign" to the immune system. The result—a kind of microscopic suicide —could possibly be the reason behind most of the symptoms of aging.

One problem with theories that attribute aging just to wear and tear at the cellular level is that they fail to account for the results of a fascinating series of experiments conducted over the last 12 years by Leonard Hayflick of the Stanford University School of Medicine. Hayflick scraped some normally dividing cells from the lungs of human embryos and grew them in glass bottles filled with a nutrient medium. They reproduced themselves in what seemed to be a normal manner, the number of cells doubling every three or four days. They went on doubling between 40 and 60 times—and then they stopped and died. It was as if the cells were obeying a built-in genetic pro-

gram that said: Be fruitful and multiply—but not beyond a certain point! The DNA instructions seemed to call for an average of 50 divisions; if the cells were put into a deep freeze after, say, 30 divisions, they "remembered" where they had left off. When unfrozen, they were still able to live through only 20 more divisions.

In 1974 Hayflick showed that such cells fulfilled their programed number of divisions even after they had been frozen for more than a decade. Furthermore, cells taken from middle-aged people divided fewer times before dying than those taken from four-month-old embryos; and cells taken from the embryos of relatively short-lived creatures like mice divided far fewer times than human embryonic cells. No matter what their origin, dividing cells had a programed career. There was one exception, however: cancer cells. Under exactly the same laboratory conditions, cancer cells were capable of reproducing themselves indefinitely.

Hayflick contends that counting cell divisions is a good way to measure the inexorable winding down of a genetic clock that ticks away in all cells. He believes the process goes on in dividing and nondividing cells alike, for he does not believe that an organism dies because its dividing cells have reached the limit of their ability to multiply; long before that limit could be reached, he says, the programed loss of the more general cellular functions, such as the ability to synthesize vital proteins, will undoubtedly bring about old age and death.

This reasoning convinces Hayflick that the scenario for old age is written into the DNA molecule from the very beginning, rather than developing as the errors accumulate. His most recent evidence comes from a complicated laboratory technique that allows him to extract the nuclei from older cells and replace them with nuclei from younger cells, and vice versa. He has found that the life span of these hybrid cells invariably matches the number of divisions left in the transplanted nuclei; the nuclear DNA thus appears to exert absolute control.

Like Hayflick, Bernard Strehler is convinced that the entire sequence of life, from birth through maturity to death, is programed into the DNA molecule. But Strehler takes a somewhat different—and rather hopeful—view of the way this programing governs aging. He points out that not all genes—the sections of the DNA genetic program—are in operation at all times. Every infant is born with genes that can direct the release of the hormones required for sexual development. But these genes are not switched on until the age of puberty; later in life, some of them are apparently switched off again. Strehler believes that something similar happens in old age; key sections of the genetic program, perhaps those that direct the operations of the cell's repair mechanism, are switched off. Unable to care for itself properly, the cell soon succumbs to the effects of wear and tear.

But according to Strehler, a switched-off gene does not simply atrophy; it is still there in the nucleus, ready to perform its appointed function if only there were some way to turn it on. There is evidence that a cell can suddenly start making an inhibitor, a substance that prevents a certain gene from getting its message through to the assembly line. In such cases, it is conceivable that the gene could be switched on again by sending in some substance that would have the ability to remove the inhibitory substance.

In September 1974, a team of scientists at M.I.T. announced they had determined the mechanism for turning on a gene, one that helps to assemble proteins in the cells of a common bacterium known as *E. coli*. The synthesis of a single genetic "on-switch," of course, would be only the beginning. But if aging is really caused by an inactivated gene (or genes), as Strehler argues, then the technique developed at M.I.T. may someday lead to a cure for old age on the most fundamental cellular level.

On the other hand, many gerontologists feel that theories of aging that focus exclusively on changes in individual cells are not comprehensive enough. They are unable to account for the symptoms of advanced years—the rapid and apparently coordinated breakdown of many different bodily systems—that suggest a master control dispatching signals of aging to the other parts of the body.

There are two diseases that seem to reproduce this aspect of the aging process, while drastically speeding it up. Progeria is one such ailment. A child stricken with this fortunately rare malady does not have a very long childhood. When he is only a year or two old, the symptoms of aging—or at least symptoms that mimic aging—may begin to appear. He may look, act and feel like an old man by the time he is seven or eight, and die at 11 or 12. Though the cause of progeria is almost a complete mystery at present, something—or perhaps the lack of something—apparently compresses the individual's entire life cycle into a few tragic years.

Victims of another disease known as Werner's syndrome also age with startling rapidity, but this process does not start until later in life. According to William Reichel of the Franklin Square Hospital in Baltimore, who is an authority on both diseases, the cause of Werner's syndrome has been traced to a genetic flaw. But no one understands how this single flaw can so catastroph-

Flinging itself up a waterfall, this Pacific Coast salmon consumes its reserves of energy during its suicidal rush to spawn. It stops eating when it enters the fresh water.

Lying lifeless in their British Columbia spawning grounds, a pair of sockeye salmon display the effects of the accelerated aging that brought on death. Their skins have decayed and discolored, and their snouts are bent into snarls where bones have reverted to soft cartilage.

The Salmon's Rush to Senility

The Pacific Coast salmon provides a unique case study in aging. Once this fish leaves the ocean and completes its upriver journey to inland spawning grounds, its bones soften, its flesh rots, its skin falls off and death follows within days.

If the cause of this accelerated aging proves to be a hormonal change, it could suggest a way of slowing down deterioration. In an attempt to learn more about the salmon's swift senility, a team of 18 American and Canadian scientists studied the fish at a spawning ground in British Columbia. They found that during its rush to spawn, the salmon literally drives itself to starvation; it ceases to produce the mucus that protects its oxygen-filtering gills, thus depriving itself of life-sustaining oxygen. Still unanswered, however, is the reason for other breakdowns, like that in the bones. Future study may uncover the trigger of the salmon's sudden aging.

Researchers Walter Garey (left) and Arthur Dawson insert a tube into a salmon's artery so that internal fluids can be removed. After testing, the fish is returned to the water.

Surgically joined at their sides, a young rat (left) and an old one share a common circulatory system. The scientists who conducted this experiment discovered that certain unknown factors in the young rat's bloodstream helped to dissolve dangerous deposits in the older rat's blood vessels, thus increasing the life expectancy of the animal.

ically disrupt the normal hereditary program. Perhaps the flaw affects a section of the DNA that just happens to be switched on in every cell in the body. Or is the difficulty localized in a gland (or in a part of the brain) that is responsible for prematurely triggering some kind of death substance?

A FAR-OUT VIEW

This view has been suggested by the influential director of the Gerontology Research Center in Baltimore, Nathan W. Shock, who has declared that aging ". . . must be regarded as a breakdown of the endocrine and the neural control mechanisms." W. Donner Denckla could not agree more. For Denckla not only believes that the immediate cause of the aging process and death is in the hormones, the chemical messengers that operate many bodily functions, but he

also has a theory about where the trouble starts.

In a series of papers published in 1974, Denckla expounded his belief that a critical organ for sustaining life is the hormonal gland called the thyroid—but another key gland, the pituitary, may contain the timer that turns life off. After much study of autopsy data and death records, Denckla finds that people—in fact, all mammals —die through the failure of one of two major body systems: the cardiovascular or the immune system. (This assumes that cancer is an immunological disease, as more and more researchers now consider it to be.) There is only one gland that produces a direct and profound effect on both systems—the thyroid, which regulates the basal metabolic rate, the speed at which cells burn their fuel and oxygen.

The importance of the thyroid is indicated by the disease that most closely mimics premature aging in adults, hypothyroidism, caused by production of too little of its essential hormone, thyroxine. A diminished supply of thyroxine causes a number of critical imbalances in the cell, which allows the onset of the destructive changes associated with aging.

Hypothyroidism can be fatal if untreated. Advanced cases of hypothyroidism are almost never seen these days, however, because thyroxine is administered as soon as a deficiency is discovered. In the 1890s, when thyroxine was first used, its effects caused astonishment: wrinkles disappeared, gray hair turned black again, and resistance to disease returned. Encouraged by these results on patients lacking the hormone, doctors used thyroxine to reverse the symptoms of aging in the really old. But the treatment quickly went out of style for two very good reasons: 1) it did not work, and 2) the high dosage killed some of the patients.

It turns out that old people are not deficient in thyroxine. Plenty of it circulates in their bloodstream, but their cells somehow are not able to take it up and use it. Denckla believes—on the basis of a series of ingenious animal experiments—that the pituitary gland begins at puberty to release death hormones, which somehow prevent cells from using thyroxine.

EVIDENCE FOR A DEATH HORMONE

So far, Denckla's death hormones are essentially speculation. But evidence implicating the pituitary also comes from studies of those remarkable migratory fish, the Pacific salmon and the steelhead trout. Both fish spend much of their lives in the ocean before returning to their native fresh-water streams to spawn. They arrive at the mouth of their home stream in superb physical condition, but on the way to the spawning grounds, they age with astonishing rapidity. Almost every system in their bodies deteriorates. Many scientists who have observed this phenomenon feel that a key factor in the rapid aging is the pituitary gland, which increases in size and productivity as the fish enters fresh water.

There is an odd and intriguing difference between the spawning salmon and the spawning trout. No Pacific salmon ever survives the spawning run. But most steelhead trout manage to make it back downstream to the ocean. And those that do are almost completely rejuvenated! In particular, the terrible symptoms of arterial degeneration virtually disappear. Some steelhead trout survive several spawnings, and each episode is characterized by a reversal of what should have been fatal arterial disease.

Because no one has yet been able to study the steelhead trout under controlled conditions, there can be no certainty that hormones are involved in the fish's sudden descent into "old age" and equally sudden recovery. To permit the necessary studies, Stewart Wolf hopes to raise enough money to build an artificial trout stream at the University of Texas Medical Branch in Galveston. At the same university, a team headed by Allan L. Goldstein has already implicated another gland, the thymus, in immune-system failures that come with aging (graph, page 114).

While some scientists seek within cells and glands for fundamental mechanisms that cause people to get old, others are looking more closely at the symptoms of age. These researchers are less interested in locating the internal clock than in discovering ways to slow it down. They are attacking the symptoms of advanced years with new treatments that may help the aging cell perform vital functions it can no longer perform by itself—such as repairing damaged or defective parts in its protein-manufacturing mechanism, or cleaning out its own waste products, and repelling or neutralizing foreign invaders.

Kalidas Nandy of Emory University in Atlanta has been testing a substance called centrophenoxine. According to Nandy, centrophenoxine removes waste products known as lipofuscins from nerve cells. Lipofuscins accumulate in cells until they take up as much as 30 per cent of the space, possibly choking off vital functions. Medical researchers in France have discovered that centrophenoxine tablets make old people more alert, improve their memory and help them concentrate on intellectual tasks.

Another substance that may help the cell battle old age is vitamin E, which might strengthen repair mechanisms. The reasoning that suggests the role of vitamin E is complex. This vitamin is one of a number of compounds known to retard oxidation, the reaction in which oxygen is combined with other substances. (It is what causes sweet butter to turn rancid.)

Oxidation helps all cells generate energy, but it also generates "free radicals"—highly unstable, broken-off pieces of molecules that race frantically around the cell until they find other molecules they can unite with. Their recklessly random recombination is what causes trouble. Free radicals can split molecules in half, knock pieces off them or form a cross-linkage—the inadvertent joining of two large molecules. Some of those large molecules are essential to cell operations, and cross-linking them takes them out of action. It would be as if someone threw a lasso over two adjacent workers on an assembly line, and no one came forward to untie them. Those workers would be unable to do their assigned jobs. In the cell, lots of cross-linkages mean lots of work stoppages, and then eventually, no work at all.

Cross-linkages have long been implicated in the symptoms of aging. But it was Denham Harman of the University of Nebraska who first suggested that free radicals might be doing most of the mischief. Harman got his clue from studying radiation sickness. He noticed that mice exposed to harmful doses of atomic radiation had great quantities of free radicals in their cells. These animals not only had a shortened life span, they also suffered from symptoms that looked suspiciously like the symptoms of old age.

Harman wondered if the smaller quantities of free radicals normally present in cells could be responsible for the process of ordinary aging. He already knew of experiments that were successful in protecting mice from radiation damage by mopping up the free radicals with oxidation-retarding drugs similar to vitamin E. Therefore, Harman injected a mixture of these drugs into the food of healthy, unirradiated mice. He discovered that the treated animals were more likely to live to a ripe old age than untreated animals.

Harman's mice did not break through the maximum life span for their species. However, the possibility of doing so with vitamin E is suggested by the experiments of Lester Packer and his associates at the University of California. They managed to keep some cell cultures (page 114) alive through more than 100 divisions—doubling the life span of human cells—by treating them with huge doses of vitamin E.

Other treatments that seem to affect life span —at least in laboratory animals—include blood exchange, diet and body cooling.

One group of tests on the effect of blood circulation was conducted by Frederic C. Ludwig of the University of California at Irvine, who surgically linked young rats and old rats so that they shared a common blood circulation. The older partners of these artificial Siamese twins lived significantly longer than control animals. Apparently, there are factors circulating in the blood of young animals that can help older animals stay alive. Other researchers have taken small pieces of skin tissue from older mice and grafted them onto young mice. Each time the host begins to age, the tissue is transplanted again. One such transplant outlived the mouse from which it was originally taken by one and a half lifetimes.

It is also known that animals live longer if they eat less. Young rats fed a diet that is very low in calories while high in nutrients develop normally, but after reaching maturity, they seem to age more slowly. Cooling also slows down aging, but by reducing metabolism, the rate at which food is converted into energy. By combining these two methods, Charles H. Barrows Jr., of the Gerontology Research Center in Baltimore was able to triple the life span of the lowly rotifer, a microscopic aquatic organism, which normally lives about 18 days. Dropping the water temperature by 10° almost doubled the life span of the rotifer. Cutting the food supply in half added still another 18 days.

What is good for a rotifer is not necessarily good for a rat, much less a person, and Barrows' results do not imply that people can starve their way to long life. But two other researchers, Gabor Kemeny and Barnett Rosenberg of Michigan State University, have suggested the possibilities for humans. They theorized that low temperatures might be good for living cells because at high temperatures proteins tend to lose the complex three-dimensional structure that enables them to perform various functions in the cellular factory. Kemeny and Rosenberg calculate that if a person's temperature could be safely lowered by only about 3.6° F. and maintained there, he could expect to live nearly 100 years. Last year, the Michigan scientists announced that they had discovered a drug that lowers body temperature by turning off the brain's thermostat. They are now testing the drug on mice to see what effect it has on life span.

According to Strehler and Denckla there is no longer any reason to doubt that a true extension of the human life span is possible. How far? Scientists of the stature of Bentley Glass of the State University of New York at Stony Brook and James Bonner of Caltech think that several hundred years is a conservative guess.

That such an achievement would be a very mixed blessing is clear from tales about favored mortals having been granted eternal life and, eventually, asking the gods for one more gift —death. As Denckla and many others point out, the death of the individual seems to be necessary to the survival of the species. Not simply to prevent overcrowding, but because all species adapt to changing environments through a process of natural selection—survival of the fittest —and the evolutionary process works best when the population is turning over rapidly. Apparently, the mortality rate resulting from disease and accidental injury is not high enough, so each individual comes equipped with what Denckla calls "an absolutely fail-safe killing mechanism."

Strehler too is aware that aging and death are what nature has planned for all life. But he says, "What if we have other plans?" He characterizes death as a kind of Moby Dick, a tough, remorseless leviathan—never before conquered, to be sure, but conquerable nonetheless—and himself as one of the numerous Captain Ahabs out to get the Great White Whale. "And sooner or later," he vows, planting his feet as if on a deck and looking toward the far horizon, "sooner or later, we *are* going to get him."

Florida's Exotic Aliens

The human urge to "improve" the environment brings a steady stream of plant and animal immigrants into almost every country. Plants are shuttled from place to place to add an exotic note to familiar surroundings. People bored with old pets seek new ones. Nowhere has this plant-and-animal roulette been played with more abandon than in the United States, where thousands of new species—including the familiar English sparrow and the gypsy moth—have established themselves over the past century.

Florida has the greatest concentration of recent immigrants—and as a result some of the biggest headaches. The Sunshine State can trace most of its problems to its position as the nation's capital of the foreign pet, plant and aquarium trade. Each year tens of millions of imported fish, reptiles, amphibians, mammals and birds enter its ports. Many of these newcomers escape or are set free. Others, however, arrive quite on their own. Only a flap or a splash away in Central and South America, they settle quickly and comfortably in Florida, where the tropical climate is similar to the one they left behind.

While most of these species seem harmless, all carry the potential for harm, because many of them multiply rapidly and are hardy enough to adapt to new homes. For example, the cattle egret *(right)* flew to Florida in the 1940s. In many respects it is welcome; it is beautiful and it helps cattle by eating their grass-loving competition, the grasshopper. Yet the bird has now become established in 25 states, and its numbers may eventually drive other species to extinction.

Ecologists have long insisted that such migrations are potentially dangerous to the environment. Now they will have tentative government support. A white paper, released in 1974 by the Bureau of Sport Fisheries and Wildlife, calls for a ban on all foreign wildlife except "low-risk" species and those cleared for "scientific, educational, zoological, or medical purposes."

Cattle egrets like this one, carefully preening its feathers in a Florida marsh, made their way from West Africa to South America and finally to the United States in the 1940s.

A red-whiskered bulbul, descendant of a bird imported to the U.S. from India, perches on a limb in southern Florida. It was first thought to be a danger to citrus crops, but instead eats another immigrant—a pepper, imported from Brazil, which is spreading rapidly.

Typical of the birds that were brought into Florida as pets and then escaped to the wilds are these red-crowned parrots. Originally imported from Mexico, the parrots now can be spotted throughout southeastern Florida.

Airborne Arrivals--Friends and Foes

They came to Florida in the most modern way —by jet plane—and were destined for cozy cages around the country. But thousands of the millions of tropical birds imported to the nation's pet capital each year escape. As a result, 12 species of non-native birds have now become a permanent part of Florida's environment.

Most of the imported birds have settled comfortably and unobtrusively into their new home. The red-whiskered bulbul *(top left),* imported from India around 1914 as a pet, was a nuisance in its native land—it ate fruit from farmers' orchards—but it seems to prefer the berries of wild peppers in Florida. The spotted-breasted oriole *(below),* an émigré from Central America, is also a harmless introduced species.

Some exotic birds that were harmless in captivity behave quite differently once they escape from their cages or are intentionally set free. They become serious, often destructive, pests as they take over the nesting sites of native birds and compete with them for food.

One potential troublemaker being nervously watched by ecologists is the monk parakeet, which feasted on fruits in its native South America. The parakeet is now spreading throughout Florida and has been seen as far north as New York and as far west as California.

Preparing to feed hungry chicks, this Central American native, the spotted-breasted oriole, lives peacefully in Florida, where it gets along with all other avian species.

A fish out of water, Clarias batrachus flops along a dry riverbed. The "walking catfish" is so aggressive that even the voracious piranha gives it a wide berth if both are in the same tank.

Pike killifish like these can live in both fresh and salt water. The plentiful fish are now gobbling up native species in southeast Florida.

An Aquatic Menace Spread by Canals

Florida is the nation's largest aquarium, with 75 million fish imported to its shores each year. But when these fish get out of their confining ponds, as many inevitably do, they find at their fintips a choice of escape routes: Florida's 3,000-mile network of canals designed to drain swamps for mosquito control and free lands for real estate development. The canals let the new arrivals reach every corner of the state, where they multiply rapidly in tropical waters.

Clarias batrachus is singularly equipped for escape. It has auxiliary breathing organs and, in the dry season, burrows in the mud. During the rainy season, it "walks," propelling itself on tough pectoral fins. On occasion, the fish have startled drivers by flip-flopping across roads. But

Clarias is more than an acrobat. It can live in salt and fresh water, and even in swamp bottoms where there is virtually no dissolved oxygen. As it flourishes, it devours other fish, including the native catfish and largemouth bass. And spells of cold weather are producing cold-resistant *Clarius* that survive farther north.

A more dangerous import is the tiny seven-inch pike killifish. In the 14 years since it arrived from South America, it has developed a voracious appetite for native species, and its taste could have dire consequences for man. Among the killifish's favorite prey is a mosquito-eating fish called *Gambius affinis;* this poses the threat that mosquitoes—and mosquito-borne diseases—will proliferate in Florida's marshlands.

Florida's extensive canal and river system is a giant conduit for spreading alien aquatic life. The black acara, a South American fish that probably escaped from a pond near Boca Raton (arrow) in 1968, multiplied in the canals and interlocking waterways and is now found from Palm Beach in the north to Everglades National Park in the south.

LAKE OKEECHOBEE

PALM BEACH

BOCA RATON

MIAMI

EVERGLADES NATIONAL PARK

Clogged with water hyacinths, this canal near Miami has become a place where no boat and few fish can pass.

Water Hyacinths: Beautiful But Dangerous

Back in 1884, Mrs. W. F. Fuller visited an exposition in New Orleans, bought a lovely floating plant called a water hyacinth and planted it in her fish pond in San Mateo, Florida. From that innocent beginning, the flower, originally a native of Brazil, has spread like crabgrass in a suburban lawn. The water hyacinth grows at such a prodigious rate—a single flower can produce 65,000 new offspring in one year—that today oceans of them choke streams, canals and ponds throughout Florida. The thick roots form an underwater tangle impenetrable to boats. The swarming plants also use up oxygen and thus threaten to drive out all other aquatic life.

Every known means of eradication has been used to control the hyacinths, including the use of *Trichechus,* the big aquatic sea cows that eat quantities of vegetation. Transported to infestation sites on flatbed trucks, the animals wallowed among the flowers, gulping them down with gusto. But although the sea cows ate up to 100 pounds of flowers a day, they did little to stop the hyacinth plague because they failed to reproduce in their new home.

In desperation, researchers returned to the source of the troublesome plant: Brazil. There they scooped up samples of two weevils that devour aquatic plants in Brazil's own jungle rivers. Entomologists hope the weevils, which have been loosed for testing in Florida's Lake Okeechobee, will feast with equal greed on water hyacinths and bring them under control by 1984.

The hyacinths' fragile beauty lured a Florida woman into planting them in her backyard pond—and setting off a state-wide infestation.

Basking on a riverbed in the hot sun, these caymans were freed by their owners after they turned out to be particularly ornery pets. Hundreds like these are now loose in Florida.

Although its spiny skin and horned head make it seem to be a prehistoric monster, the harmless Texas horned lizard has adapted easily to its new environment in Florida.

Southeast Asian tokay geckos were released in a Miami building in the 1960s to control roaches. They did—so well that zoos and pet stores still use them for this purpose.

An iguana, resting on a stump in southern Florida, is one of a thriving population begun by accident in 1964, when some 300 were inadvertently released by an animal dealer.

A baleful Bufo marinus peers from its swampy home. Bufo grows to 8 inches long and is poisonous (the white liquid on its neck is venom).

Amphibians and Reptiles on the Loose

Once the denizens of aquariums and zoos, alien reptiles and amphibians are now hissing, croaking and burping from one end of Florida to the other. Mexican iguanas have been seen slithering across baseball diamonds; the tree frog, imported from Cuba, crawls into the relay boxes of power plants and electrocutes itself dramatically, shorting circuits and causing blackouts.

Most of these introduced species are former pets. Dealers began importing the South American cayman *(top, far left),* a cousin of the Florida alligator, when selling of baby alligators was banned in the 1940s. But the cayman often proved to be more vicious than its owners anticipated, and was shown the door. Now the reptiles are flourishing in swamps and may be competing with the dwindling alligator for dominance.

Some animal immigrants were loosed to control other pests—and became pests themselves. The giant South American toad, or *Bufo marinus (above),* is one. Imported to eat crop-destroying insects, *Bufo* also eats the young of smaller native toads. A number of cats and dogs have been killed by biting into the poison sacs on its neck.

Fortunately, most of these introduced reptiles and amphibians, including the Texas horned lizard *(top, right),* the Southeast Asian tokay gecko *(bottom, left)* and the Central American green iguana *(bottom, right),* appear to be harmless. But numbers ultimately determine the impact of any new species on the environment. Ecologists warn that if the creatures keep multiplying—there now are about 22 species in the wilds—native animals may be forced into extinction.

Fighting the Fire Ant with a Tricky Native

The Brazilian fire ant is in some ways the most troublesome and difficult to eradicate of the newly introduced wildlife. Named for its sting, which raises large painful welts on cattle and humans, *Solenopsis invicta* mysteriously arrived in the United States in 1940 and has since spread to nine southern states, including Florida. It builds gigantic anthills, sometimes more than three feet high, in which as many as 60,000 ants may live.

Solenopsis invicta's powerful sting and its concentration of huge populations in each colony enabled the ant to overwhelm most of the insect competition it encountered in the U.S. But now scientists are exploring ways to fight back—not with chemical pesticides—but with native ants like *Lasius noeniger,* a north Florida native shown in action at right. *Neoniger* uses a sort of chemical warfare on its enemies, squirting them with a lethal acid. In battles initiated by the scientists, *neoniger* groups fight stubbornly, but must give way because they are outnumbered by 100 to one in colony-versus-colony struggles. Yet the native *neoniger* might win out in the end if more of the smaller ants could be concentrated in areas now infested by the Brazilian newcomer.

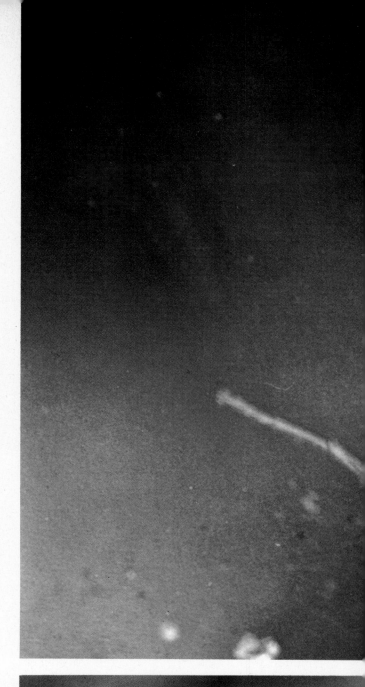

Fighting for its life, a fire ant kicks up a cloud of dust as it seeks to escape its smaller foe, L. neoniger. By clutching the fire ant's leg in its mandibles, neoniger coats it with a secretion that increases the effect of a later spray of poison. In the sequence below, a fire ant frees itself, lifts its tail and then stings neoniger before it can let loose its spray.

New World Invasion of Old World Pests

If Florida is a beachhead for biological invasion, as some scientists have suggested, it is hardly alone. Indeed, the ecological skirmishes in the Sunshine State are minor sorties in the battles for survival—pitting plants, animals and people against one another—that have followed the introduction of foreign forms of life.

A frightening example of what can happen when an introduced species gets out of hand occurred in March 1974, in Graceham, Maryland. For six days, Graceham's 400 citizens battled two million birds. Many of the birds were starlings, descendants of a handful brought to the United States from England in 1890 by a wealthy and eccentric naturalist who specialized in importing birds that had been mentioned in Shakespeare's plays. The creatures, like the murderous pests in Alfred Hitchcock's *The Birds,* attacked cats and dogs and even chased cows from feed bins. The townspeople of Graceham repeatedly tried to drive the birds off with firecrackers and with amplified recordings of bird distress calls. All attempts failed. Finally, in April, the birds departed, as mysteriously as they had arrived.

In California the menace is, of all things, frogs. A species called the African clawed frog was brought in for an admirable reason—to serve as a laboratory animal in tests for pregnancy. It was used as an indicator: When urine from a pregnant woman was injected into a female frog, its ovaries reacted to hormones in the urine and produced eggs. With the development of more efficient pregnancy tests, the frogs were discarded. They quickly learned to fend for themselves in Southern California; with a rapacious appetite, they eat other amphibians, insects, larvae, and even young mice and birds.

By far the worst effects of such biological pollution have been felt in Hawaii. When the first white settlers arrived in the isolated islands in the 18th Century, the impact was much like that of European smallpox on the American Indian: instant destruction. Rats escaping from settlers' ships decimated much of the islands' sugar cane crop within a few years. Mongooses were intro-

duced to control the rats but they ate other species, including birds and snakes that helped control local pests.

One arrival to Hawaii, the giant African snail, attacked crops so voraciously that 23 foreign species were imported to bring it under control. They, too, eventually became pests, and now threaten several species of native snail. As a result of these invasions, and other introductions, little remains of Hawaii's original wildlife. Today some 98 per cent of Hawaii's mammals, about 60 per cent of its birds and nearly all of its plants are non-native.

The Hawaiian disaster is unlikely to be repeated elsewhere in the United States, partly because only isolated islands are vulnerable to such complete ecological turnover. Under normal conditions, newly arrived pests are controlled by overwhelming numbers of natural enemies. And of course for millennia, species of all kinds have migrated away from their ancestral lands to new homes without causing undue harm. But a century of fast transportation has accelerated the natural process of migration, and habitats have less time to develop the predators necessary to keep down infestations of new species.

Man may have to help out by experimenting with biological counterforces to combat pests such as the pine sawfly *(right).* Introduced from Europe on shipments of pine trees, the sawfly is a serious pest; it has stripped and killed pines in the Midwest and Canada. It is difficult to eradicate because so very little is known about its habits. A clue to control of the sawfly and perhaps other insect pests has now come from Cornell, where animal behaviorist Thomas Eisner has discovered why the sawfly is so tough: It bends pine trees' natural defenses to its own use. Pine resin, which is poisonous to other insects, is eaten by the sawfly and then squirted out to destroy foes that might help keep it in check. Following Eisner's lead, other scientists are studying the sawfly in hope of finding a parasite that will attack it while it is still in the egg stage —long before it begins munching on pine trees.

In Thomas Eisner's laboratory at Cornell University, larvae of an imported pest, the pine sawfly, strip needles from a pine bough, then store its usually toxic resin in their bodies.

Poised on a pine needle, a larva spits the pine's poison (the bubble on its proboscis) at an attacker. In this way the sawfly larva turns the tree's natural defense into a weapon.

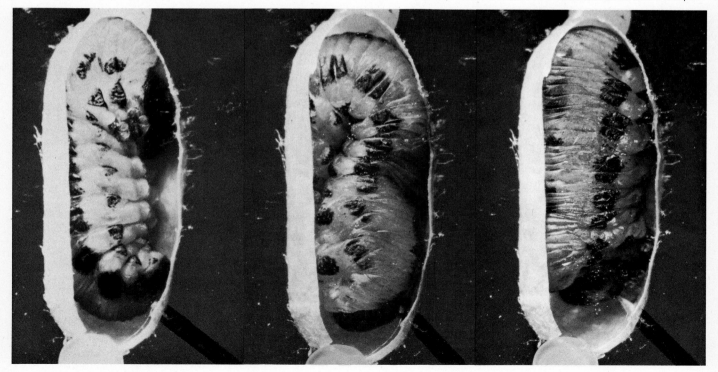

Prodded by a needle (left), a sawfly larva curls in its cocoon (center) to squirt its attacker (right). Knowledge of its tactics may point to a natural enemy able to control it.

The Famine of 1974

CRISES OF CLIMATE AND ENERGY HINT OF WORSE TO COME

by C. P. Gilmore

During 1974, starving nomads in northern Chad boiled roots and tree bark to stay alive. In the small Ethiopian village of Arba Minch, 15 people were shot while rioting over food. Near the capital of Niger in the sub-Saharan region of Africa known as the Sahel, as many as 20,000 drought victims huddled together in a disease-wracked refugee camp, their lands gone, their cattle dead. The year was punctuated with reports of riots by starving people in India, and there were predictions that the overpopulated country was facing one of the worst famines in its entire history.

Although very heavy rains in the Sahel toward the end of August seemed to herald a return to its normal precipitation patterns after a catastrophic six-year drought, this region—a 2,000-mile-wide swath extending from Mauritania and Senegal in the west to Chad in the east—could count hundreds of thousands of people dead in the wake of the dry years.

Torrential spring rains struck the United States, delaying the corn planting across broad sections of the Midwest; drought through much of the summer of 1974 severely cut production of corn, wheat and soybeans, and an early frost delivered a further blow to the reduced corn and soybean crops. Canadian wheat also suffered substantially from the early cold spell, and in the Soviet Union, the Siberian wheat crop was reported to have taken a heavy beating from drought. There would be enough food in the United States—at increasing prices—for the immediate future, but grain for export to the hungry nations was in short supply.

A timely response to these and earlier signs of potential famine was the first international con-

On a parched desert in Mali, nomads scrabble in the sand for pieces of wheat bran. The tough grain, originally airdropped for starving cattle, now feeds women and children driven to a desperate search for sustenance.

ference ever called to discuss worldwide food problems—convened in Rome in November at the behest of the United States. The meeting assembled none too soon, for in the years just prior to 1974, the news had been almost as dismal. Drought or flood had reduced harvests in India, China, the Soviet Union and the Philippines. Hunger spread through drought-stricken areas of Brazil, Mexico and Central America. For the first time since World War II, world food production actually declined.

Today, experts estimate that perhaps as many as half of the earth's 3.7 billion people live in never-ending hunger. But in 1974 it was becoming obvious that a new combination of global factors threatens an unprecedented—and possibly irreversible—drift toward starvation on a scale never before witnessed. The most brutal influence on this frightening trend has unquestionably been the weather.

Many scientists now fear that these ominous new patterns of unaccustomed drought in some places—and flood in others—may not be simply a random fluctuation; rather, that the changes may be part of a long-term shift in the planet's climate. Exacerbating the meteorological pressure are such other famine-inducing factors as the worldwide energy shortage, the failure of new hybrid crop strains—the widely hailed "green revolution"—to live up to some of the more optimistic expectations, and the paradoxically negative effect on world food supplies of a few countries' growing affluence. Another crucial element in the hunger equation has been the continuing exponential growth of population despite efforts by some nations to contain it. In 1974 alone, the world's population grew by about 75 million. The human race has almost doubled since the end of World War II and threatens to double again around the year 2000.

Some authorities believe that not even the wealthy nations of Western Europe and North America will be able to escape the consequences of the burgeoning, worldwide food shortages. George Harrar, the president of the Rockefeller Foundation, predicts that "the affluent societies will experience dramatically reduced standards of living at home."

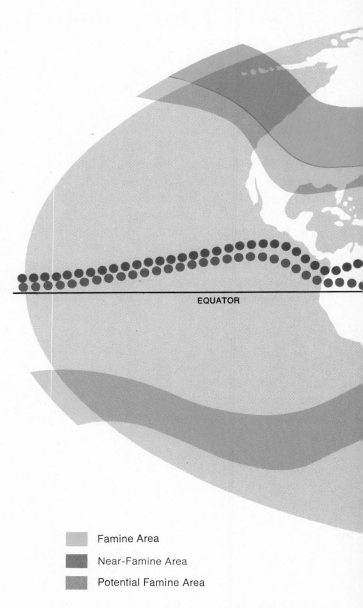

EQUATOR

Famine Area

Near-Famine Area

Potential Famine Area

Climatologists believe that the key to the world's current pattern of droughts is the circumpolar vortex, a great skirt of cold air that rotates from west to east near the North Pole. This vortex, experts theorize, has expanded from its range 20 years ago (blue belt) to an area hundreds of miles farther south (red belt). High-pressure systems of dry air at the leading edge of this expanding vortex block the northward-moving monsoon winds from entering their former range (dotted blue line), holding them to more southerly areas (dotted red line). As a result, such northern areas as

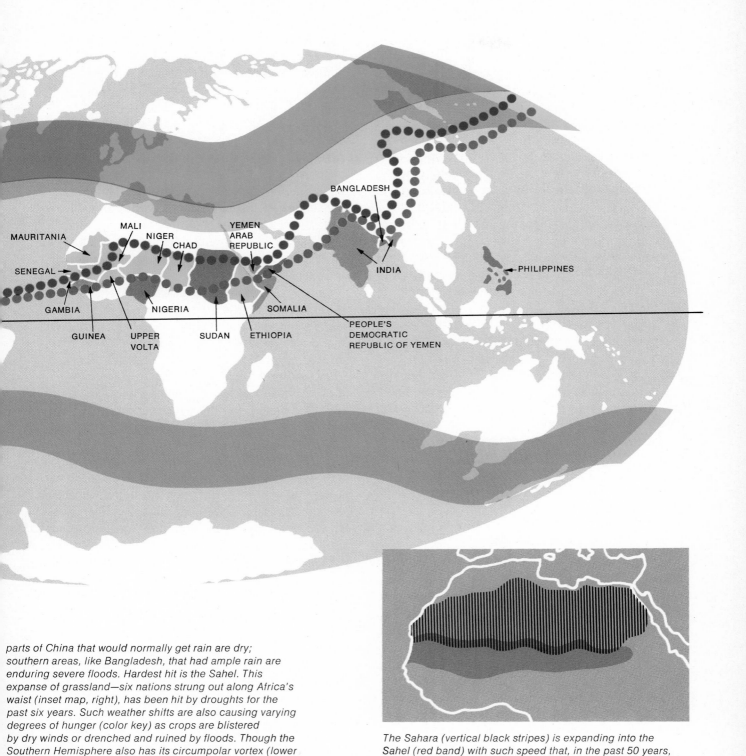

MAURITANIA

MALI

NIGER

CHAD

YEMEN ARAB REPUBLIC

BANGLADESH

SENEGAL

GAMBIA

GUINEA

UPPER VOLTA

NIGERIA

SUDAN

ETHIOPIA

SOMALIA

PEOPLE'S DEMOCRATIC REPUBLIC OF YEMEN

INDIA

PHILIPPINES

parts of China that would normally get rain are dry; southern areas, like Bangladesh, that had ample rain are enduring severe floods. Hardest hit is the Sahel. This expanse of grassland—six nations strung out along Africa's waist (inset map, right), has been hit by droughts for the past six years. Such weather shifts are also causing varying degrees of hunger (color key) as crops are blistered by dry winds or drenched and ruined by floods. Though the Southern Hemisphere also has its circumpolar vortex (lower band) little is known of its effect on global weather.

The Sahara (vertical black stripes) is expanding into the Sahel (red band) with such speed that, in the past 50 years, a Texas-sized area (overlapping area) has been engulfed.

The rapid and bewildering change in the world's food picture began in 1972. Largely because of adverse weather conditions in many parts of the globe, production dipped by about 1 per cent—in some key crops such as wheat, the drop was 3 per cent. But since population continued to expand by 2 per cent, the result was a per capita decline of about 3 percent in the food supply. Backup resources shrank drastically: Though in 1961 world reserves had been sufficient to feed all the globe's people for 95 days, by late 1974 there was only a 26-day supply—the lowest in 20 years.

World reaction to the shortage was dramatic. Prices soared as nations tried to outbid one another for the scarce supplies. Land that had been kept out of production in the United States for the past 30 years was hastily planted in an effort to increase the supply. But this was still not enough. With a continuing shortage of wheat on the world market, the price of the grain reached $5.38 per bushel in late 1974, two to three times the going rate a year earlier. The rise in cost will have catastrophic effects. Norman Borlaug, winner of the 1970 Nobel Peace Prize for his work in plant genetics, which helped to create many new and productive strains of food crops, expressed the extent of the coming disaster mordantly. "The doubling or tripling of food prices in some countries," Borlaug told the Senate Agriculture Committee, "does not inconvenience people who have to spend 80 per cent of their income on a diet of grain; it kills them."

A DANGEROUS COOLING TREND

The principal killer is the weather—or, more precisely, a complicated set of changes in worldwide meteorological patterns. Records show that overall world temperature has dropped 1° F. since 1940. This temperature change, in turn, has had a significant influence on the world's weather, particularly on rainfall patterns in portions of the Northern Hemisphere. The temperature drop has meant the expansion to the south of a meteorological phenomenon known as the circumpolar vortex, a huge whirling system of cold air that hugs the North Pole like a giant cap. (A similar vortex covers the South Pole, but its effect

on world weather patterns has not been studied in detail by meteorologists; in any case, most of the world's population lives—and most crops grow—north of the equator.)

The southern edge of the northern vortex extends approximately to a line that crosses the southern United States, North Africa and parts of Central Asia—a broad band of territory containing most of the world's deserts. South of the line—and of the deserts—is the area in which the monsoon rains fall: Southeast Asia, Central America, sub-Saharan Africa. Such has been the case, at any rate, until recently. Now, some scientists argue, the lowering of world temperatures has enlarged the circumpolar vortex and moved its lower edge farther south.

This shift is extremely critical because the circumpolar vortex plays a large part in determining the location of both deserts and fertile monsoon areas. The dynamics of weather depend to a great extent on the role of the vortex. The sun warms the earth in the vicinity of the equator; the warm earth heats the air. Filled with moisture it has picked up from the sea, the heated air rises, drops its moisture in the form of rain, and moves at high altitudes toward the cooler north, partly impelled by the tendency of the atmosphere to equalize differences in temperature between the equator and the poles.

But the moving mass of air, now dry and cooling, does not reach the North Pole. As it travels, it inevitably sinks at the southern edge of the circumpolar vortex, and its northward movement is blocked. As this dry air descends toward the surface, it becomes a large, dry, high-pressure system. This high, in turn, blocks the air that contains moisture, inhibiting rainfall and helping create the deserts.

Much of the moist air that is diverted by this high pressure system is driven by one of the earth's most potent weather engines: the trade winds, which pick up moisture as they move across the seas. As the trade winds surge over the equatorial areas of the Atlantic, Pacific and Indian oceans, they encounter either Africa, Central America or Southeast Asia. In warm seasons, these winds drop their moisture in the form of the torrential monsoon rains on which a large part of the world's population is so dependent for growing its crops. But the monsoon winds can only penetrate as far north as the edge of the dry, high-pressure, descending air mass that defines the deserts. Therefore the northern edge of the crop-producing monsoon region is determined by the location of the dry-air system. And the placement of the dry air, in turn, is set by the position of the leading southern edge of the circumpolar vortex.

For quite a few years, this delicately balanced system has deviated from the pattern it exhibited three or four decades ago. In expanding and moving its boundary several hundred miles to the south, the circumpolar vortex has shoved the desert areas southward by changing rainfall patterns and thereby causing, among other things, the drought in Africa. The vortex is probably also involved in the diminished rainfall and the consequent poor harvests in parts of Latin America, China and India.

FROM TOO MUCH RAIN: A PLAGUE OF LOCUSTS

The total amount of atmospheric moisture available for the production of rain has, of course, not diminished as a result of the shift in the boundaries and dimensions of the circumpolar vortex. The rain withheld from parts of Africa and India simply falls elsewhere, sometimes with unexpected effect. For example, a British investigator named Derek Winstanley, who was seeking the cause of an explosion of locusts in the North African desert in 1969, found that heavy rains in that normally dry area had created ideal breeding conditions for the insects.

No one is sure how the global weather system actually balances these accounts; but while the expanding circumpolar vortex causes drought in some areas, it may conversely be responsible for the increased rainfall and catastrophic floods that in recent years have disrupted the harvest seasons in places as geographically diverse as Canada, the United States, the Philippines, Italy and Bangladesh.

These altered rainfall patterns may represent a long-term realignment of global climate. "It is abundantly clear," says Reid A. Bryson, director of the Institute for Environmental Studies at the University of Wisconsin, "that the earth's climate is changing in a direction that is not promising in terms of our ability to feed the world."

Bryson is one of those who believe that a decline in the average temperature of the earth is expanding the circumpolar vortex. Support for the thesis comes from recent research on the Greenland icecap, where scientists drilled into the ice and sampled layers laid down as snow during the past one thousand years. By analyzing the ratios of certain isotopes of oxygen in the samples, they were able to calculate the temperature record of the Northern Hemisphere over the past 10 centuries with reasonable accuracy.

The record shows, among other things, that global temperatures from 1890 to 1940 had been the warmest since early medieval times. Yet, though meteorologists still consider the average temperatures during that period as normal, Bryson insists that this spell of warming was fleeting and aberrant—"the most abnormal period in at least 800 years." Indeed, temperatures have been slowly falling since 1940. And a downward shift of one or two degrees more could mean the start of a new ice age.

While a shift to colder times was probably inevitable anyway according to Bryson's theory, he is now convinced that man is making the weather situation even worse by pumping dust, smoke and other pollutants into the atmosphere. Among other things, the pollutants have blocked some of the sun's radiant heat, thus aggravating the natural cooling trend. Altogether, Bryson sees a dismal future for the human race. "It would appear," he says, "that we are at the end of an era —the era of surpluses and the era of benign climate. There is a very important climatic change going on right now. If it continues, it will affect the whole human occupation of the earth —like millions of people starving."

The extent of the disaster that threatens can be seen from 1974 crop yields on the plains of the United States, of Canada and Australia—the world's only present food-surplus areas. Both Canada and the United States experienced drought in 1974. The U.S. drought was particularly severe. Early in the year, the Agriculture Department predicted a record corn yield of 6.7

Thirsty cattle in Eagle Butte, South Dakota, assemble near a dry water hole. In 1974, drought impartially attacked livestock and croplands in both rich and poor countries.

The splendor of a maharana's palace looms incongruously over a dried-up artificial lake in the northwest Indian city of Udaipur. The lake, which had supplied water to 180,000 people, was dry for the first time since the 15th Century.

Globe-circling Drought

The 1974 droughts that cut a wide swath across Africa and Asia, causing widespread hunger, also struck the world's breadbasket—the rich grain-producing plains of North America that normally yield the world's greatest agricultural surpluses. Lack of rain in the spring drastically cut production of corn, soybeans and sorghum in much of the United States. Especially hard hit was South Dakota *(top left)*, where a dry spell slashed corn production by 38 per cent from 1973 levels. Although the United States promised to keep sending food abroad, the American drought was sure to reduce shipments, which would be a heavy blow to nations like Mali and Niger, already suffering the effects of prolonged drought.

Near the west coast of Africa, a Senegalese girl, belongings balanced on her head, passes carcasses of cattle, which were driven by months of thirst to drink water from the sea.

143

billion bushels. But by September, lack of rain across South Dakota, Iowa, Nebraska, Kansas, Texas and elsewhere cut the yield to below five billion bushels—11 per cent under the 1973 crop. Soybeans were 16 per cent below the previous year, sorghum 31 per cent. Only wheat was up —by 5 per cent. But even there, early forecasts for a 2.2 billion-bushel crop had to be trimmed back to 1.79 billion bushels.

It is possible, of course, that the drought in the United States may not be caused by global weather changes and may even be due to temporary, local conditions. But if adverse meteorological shifts do indeed turn out to be long lasting, the job of feeding the world's hungry will obviously be vastly more complicated. For the problems do not end with the weather; they begin anew with the growing shortage of energy. The high-productivity agriculture of the advanced nations, which is the goal of lesser-developed countries, uses an enormous amount of energy. At the same time, the world has become sharply aware of the finite nature of its energy resources and prices have tripled and quadrupled for one of the most widely used forms—petroleum.

This interrelationship of energy and food production can be seen most dramatically in the United States, where agriculture is practiced on a particularly high-energy level. Although the production and marketing of food in this country ranks third (behind steel and petrochemicals) in the use of all forms of energy, it uses more petroleum than any manufacturing industry. Indeed, agriculture in the United States has been transformed from the relatively unproductive undertaking it was at the turn of the century to the high output, mechanized industry it is now, largely through the application of energy for farm machinery, transportation, irrigation and the manufacture of fertilizer and pesticides.

In an attempt to keep the Sahara from invading potentially arable land, Tunisian workers erect a barrier of woven palm fronds to block wind-blown sand. While the desert is expanding, the Tunisian government is trying to reclaim the land depleted by overgrazing during the last century.

Since 1909, for example, corn yields have more than tripled, rising from 26 bushels an acre to 87 in 1971. The introduction of high-yield hybrid corn is responsible for between 20 and 40 per cent of this increase. The soaring use of energy accounts for the other 60 to 80 per cent. David Pimentel of the New York State College of Agriculture and Life Science and his colleagues recently made a study of the increasing use of energy in agriculture; they found that all of the elements involved in the production of an acre of corn require the equivalent of about 80 gallons of gasoline—an increase of 55 gallons over the amount of gasoline that was consumed for the same purpose in 1945.

If the entire world were fed at this level, and if that food were produced using these modern high-yield agricultural techniques, it would require 448 billion gallons of gasoline a year. At that rate, the entire world supply of petroleum would be dissipated in 29 years, even if it were used only for agriculture. And modern farming depends not only on the petroleum-powered support of tractors, irrigation pumps, diesel locomotives and trucks; it depends on mammoth amounts of fertilizer.

Today's fertilizers contain three principal ingredients: nitrogen, phosphorus and potassium. Potash—the source of potassium—is in plentiful supply. However, nitrogen—the element that accounts for most of the high yield of modern strains—is in the middle of a particularly severe crunch. Nitrogen itself is extremely plentiful; the earth's atmosphere is about 80 per cent nitrogen. But to make gaseous nitrogen into fertilizer, it is combined with hydrogen to make ammonia. The hydrogen usually comes from natural gas, which is in extremely short supply.

As a result, fertilizer prices have risen sharply. For example, one of the most widely used forms of nitrogen fertilizer, selling for $50 to $60 a ton in 1972, jumped to $250 a ton a year later under the pressures of growing demand and zooming natural gas prices. And rising population continues to squeeze fertilizer facilities and hikes prices every day. According to one estimate, a country must build one new 1,000-ton-a-day fertilizer plant for every increase of six million people. For a nation like India, that ratio demands two and a half new plants a year—at an annual cost of $500 million—just to stay even.

Square in the middle of all these natural and economic pressures is the green revolution, greeted just a few years ago as the scientific development that might end hunger permanently. Indeed, the green revolution has been successful; but its very ability to keep more people alive has led to a need for ever-greater tonnages of food to maintain those lives. Norman Borlaug estimates that increased crop yields in India alone have sustained 75 million people who otherwise would have died of starvation. Now these people, too, must be fed.

The basic strengths of the miracle strains are not cheaply acquired. They are especially bred to make good use of fertilizer and water. With big doses of these ingredients they produce far more grain per acre than do traditional strains.

An Indian farmer, ankle-deep in a paddy, sprays high-yield dwarf rice with insecticide. Because such new cereal strains require spraying and the machinery for irrigation, experts warn that the promise of miracle grains may be dimmed by soaring oil prices and chronic shortages.

Floodwaters surround refugees and livestock in the Punjab, Pakistan. Benefiting from ample rain in the past, the area has suffered recent climate shifts, intensifying the monsoons.

At the same time, however, some of them are also more vulnerable to diseases and pests than are the native strains. So the new strains require large applications of insecticides and pesticides, both of which are manufactured with petroleum, which in turn is becoming increasingly scarce. When any of these necessities—fertilizer, water and pesticides—are not available, yields usually are little better than those of the native varieties that they replaced.

The green revolution arose out of the realization by agricultural scientists that, as the world population exploded shortly after World War II, traditional methods of increasing grain production would no longer suffice. Food production can be increased in two basic ways. Additional land can be brought under cultivation; or a larger amount of food can be coaxed out of each acre in use. As the food needs of the human race have grown over the millennia, the former method has been favored. About 25 years ago, however, agricultural scientists developed new strains of wheat and corn that under the right conditions provide more than triple the previous yields on a given amount of land.

At the outset, the experiments with super grains primarily benefited the nations of the temperate zones, particularly the United States. But starting in the late 1950s, the Rockefeller and Ford Foundations sponsored research aimed at developing strains of rice and wheat that could produce a far greater yield per acre in the tropics, where the need has always been most desperate. The grants paid off—brilliantly—in the green revolution. For example, the International Rice Research Institute in Los Baños, the Philippines, developed a variety of rice that produced four times as much as the traditional Philippine strains. The International Maize and Wheat Improvement Center in El Batán, Texcoco, Mexico, performed similar prodigies by using new strains of wheat.

From 1960 to 1965, world grain production lagged behind population growth. But from 1966 to 1971, as the green-revolution strains were introduced more widely into tropical countries, production began to forge ahead of population growth. By 1971, four consecutive years of record harvests had totally changed the world picture; global production of grains had reached an average 615 pounds per person. With the introduction of improved rice, Indonesia's President Suharto predicted that his country would soon be self-sufficient. President Ferdinand Marcos of the Philippines, who had conducted an educational campaign as early as 1966 promising that the country would never again have to import rice, announced self-sufficiency in 1968, and actually exported some rice in 1970.

It was indeed an astounding change. Some acreage in India and Pakistan was yielding from seven to 10 times as much grain as before. In 1971, India announced that substantial grain reserves had been accumulated—for the first time since its independence in 1947—and that it would need no further grain imports by 1973.

Then, in 1972, the monsoon failed to deliver its quota of rain—a setback swiftly followed by the fertilizer shortages and soaring oil prices of 1973 and 1974. Although yields were still substantially above the levels of the years before the green revolution, India's population had continued to grow. Again, there was not enough to go around. In 1973, Indian authorities realized that their country would have to import two million tons of grain per year for five years. But by September 1974, when the extent of that summer's drought had become clearer, this figure had ballooned; seven to 10 million tons for 1974 and 1975 was calculated as the minimum amount of grain that would have to be imported if catastrophic starvation was to be avoided. In the Philippines, 1974 floods and other adverse weather conditions caused production to drop slightly, and the Philippines was again importing grain.

FEEDING THE RICH MAN'S COW

In the affluent countries where the green revolution began, the threat of starvation has become almost unthinkable—at least for the majority. But the eating habits of people in the richer nations affect the food supply of the entire world. As people get wealthier, they eat less grain. But they make up for this change in diet by eating more meat, and that diet requires the consumption of enormous quantities of grain—by cattle. A beef animal must eat seven pounds of grain to produce one pound of meat. Thus the more affluent man consumes the equivalent of seven pounds of grain every time he eats a pound of meat. In doing so, he disproportionately reduces the total amount of grain available to feed people in the rest of the world. And, if there is not enough grain to go around, the wealthy man easily outbids his less fortunate fellow human beings. As one United Nations food expert has succinctly put it, "The poor man's grain is siphoned off to feed the rich man's cow."

The resulting imbalance in consumption between affluent and poor nations is staggering. Inhabitants of underdeveloped Asian countries eat an average of 400 pounds of grain a year, the average United States citizen more than a ton. The American eats 150 pounds as bread, breakfast food, and other cereal products; the rest is fed to cattle, pigs and chickens to produce the meat, milk and eggs that serve as staples for him as grains do for the world's poorer peoples.

Agriculturists predict that the trend toward greater conversion of grain into meat and dairy products will continue to accelerate. Today, the United Kingdom, Scandinavia, much of both Eastern and Western Europe, the Soviet Union and Japan have eating habits similar to those that prevailed in the United States in 1940. That year, U.S. per capita consumption was 55 pounds of meat and 18 pounds of poultry. By 1972 it had risen to 117 pounds of meat and 51 pounds of poultry. There is no reason to believe that the affluent group of European and Asian countries will not follow the American example—and increasingly outbid the underdeveloped countries for scarce supplies of grain.

One short-term solution to this problem of economic imbalance and maldistribution could lie in the establishment of world food reserves, to be drawn upon by countries that have suffered bad harvests and need tiding over. Further in the future await possibilities for the development of more exotic sources of food that might be tapped to close the gap between the world's conventional crop yields and the number of mouths to be fed. Among these options:

• Certain strains of yeasts could be used to convert petroleum into protein. The process has, in fact, been under study by 26 oil companies.

• The common green alga *chlorella* is a cheap, nutritious, readily manufactured product, which has the added value of containing a very high percentage of protein.

• Proteins can be isolated or fabricated from animal, municipal and industrial wastes to feed livestock—and some day perhaps even meet the needs of humans.

• Although marine biologists suspect that the 65 million tons of fish now harvested annually around the world represent a maximum sustainable yield, additional protein can be taken from the ocean in the form of plankton.

Many other possible sources of protein exist, and considerable research has been done on some. For example, the nutritional value of wheat, rice and other grains is already being improved by careful breeding so that smaller amounts are needed for adequate nutrition. Hybrid soybeans might be developed which would multiply their yields the way hybrid corn has multiplied the yield of that grain. Some day, perhaps, the basic process of photosynthesis could be speeded up so that plants would convert a larger proportion of the sun's energy that falls on them into edible calories.

Unfortunately, none of these developments is likely to have much effect on the world food supply within the foreseeable future. To be useful, new foods must be not only technologically feasible, but economically viable. And people must be willing to eat them. Most of the more exotic food resources fall short—in some degree, at least—on all three counts. None promises to be important in this decade, and perhaps not for decades to come.

The best hope of averting famine still lies in the manner in which man can utilize conventional agriculture. Fortunately, large increases in yields are easiest and cheapest in the poor and developing countries where the need is greatest. Rice yields in India and Nigeria are still only one third of those in Japan; cornfields in Thailand and Brazil produce less than a third as much per acre as those in Iowa. Relatively modest investments in better seed, fertilizer and irrigation could produce dramatic increases in yields.

UNANSWERED MORAL QUESTIONS

To produce yields large enough for the adequate feeding of large populations, however, such investments must be made in the form of very substantial sums of money. Finding it and allocating it properly will not be easy, and the process may pose some nagging moral questions to the citizens of the affluent countries from which the funds must come. Each year, for example, American dog and cat lovers use hundreds of tons of tuna and other fish products for pet food while people in less fortunate countries starve. Yet even if the wealthier nations were to pinch somewhat at home—in order to mount an international effort to improve distribution of food and other resources and help developing nations to improve their yields—the gains would only be temporary. This is because habitable land is finite. Thus the ultimate problem is growing population. "I don't think there's any solution to the world food situation unless we get population stabilized," said Sterling Wortman, vice president of the Rockefeller Foundation. "Those of us who have been working to increase the food supply have never assumed we were doing any more than buying time."

Under the normal monsoon flood conditions, necessary for a successful crop, the Ganges swells beyond its banks, enriching Indian farmland with moisture and rich, dark silt.

Fresh Faces for Three Planets

Through earth-based telescopes, Venus looks like a fuzzy tennis ball, Mercury a nearly featureless blob and Jupiter, a grayish-orange globe. But thanks to detailed information gathered by the Pioneer X and Mariner X space fly-bys in late 1973 and 1974, all three planets have been given spectacular new images. Mariner took the first close-up pictures ever made of Mercury and Venus, and turned up fascinating and sometimes puzzling surface and atmospheric features *(following pages)*. While these revelations were startling, the biggest surprise came, appropriately, from Pioneer X's studies of the solar system's largest planet: Jupiter.

When space scientists began analyzing Pioneer's data they found that not only had some old notions about Jupiter been verified, but that completely new discoveries had been made. In support of earlier theories, Pioneer showed Jupiter to be a rapidly spinning ball composed mostly of hydrogen with a gaseous atmosphere.

Totally unexpected, however, was evidence that the gaseous giant may have a small core of rock, seething at 54,000° F.—about six times hotter than the surface of the sun. Astronomers speculate that this core may result from enormous pressures that compact atoms tightly in the planet's center. Another discovery is that orange belts in Jupiter's atmosphere derive their color from the presence of sulfur, which is the dominant element in the bands, and that grayish zones consist of clouds of ammonia crystals. Judging from temperature measurements, the orange bands seem to be troughs into which the cooler grayish clouds are descending.

One of the most tantalizing of all planetary riddles is Jupiter's Great Red Spot, a feature some 25,000 miles wide that glows like an eye. The Pioneer photos suggest that the spot is the vortex of a gargantuan hurricane that may have been whirling for seven centuries or more.

Jupiter's famous Red Spot and the shadow of Io, one of its 12 moons, are clearly visible from 1,500,000 miles away. The gray bands may be clouds of ammonia that rise above warmer orange clouds containing sulfur compounds.

In this sequence of pictures, arrows indicate the passage of a dark, 620-mile-wide cloud formation across Venus' 7,600-mile disc. Here, the cloud system, moving nearly 250 miles per hour, begins an east-west transit of the planet.

After seven hours, the dark cloud formation (arrow) retains its general shape, and has moved about 2,000 miles to the west, following the direction of the rotation of Venus.

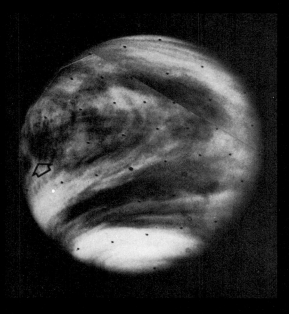

At the end of 14 hours, the cloud (arrow), seems to break up after it has whipped halfway across the face of Venus, and begins to slide out of sight around the equator.

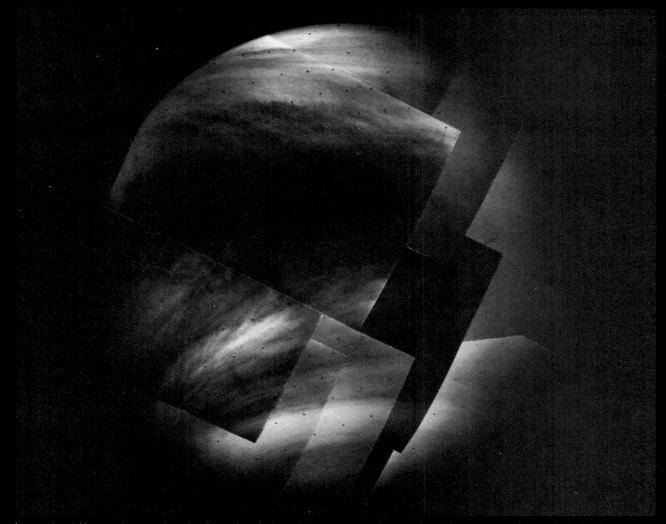

A mosaic of Venus shows polar clouds and a dark, turbulent equatorial area where Venusian weather is thought to originate.

Lifting the Veils from Venus

Before Mariner X's close flyby of Venus, astronomers studying the planet through their earth-based telescopes could only discern this nearly featureless white blob.

Shooting from 3,600 miles out, Mariner X's ultraviolet cameras provided the first sharp details of Venus' cloud patterns. The pictures revealed cloud formations on the planet's disc comparable in some ways to weather patterns on earth. Scientists speculate that Venus' dense atmosphere, heated like earth's by the sun, expands and spirals away from its equator toward its north and south poles. Unlike earth, however, Venus spins from east to west and the rotation is so slow—only once every 243 terrestrial days—that cloud patterns stay intact far longer than on earth. Mariner's cameras were thus able to provide the spectacular views *(opposite)* of a Venusian weather system on the move.

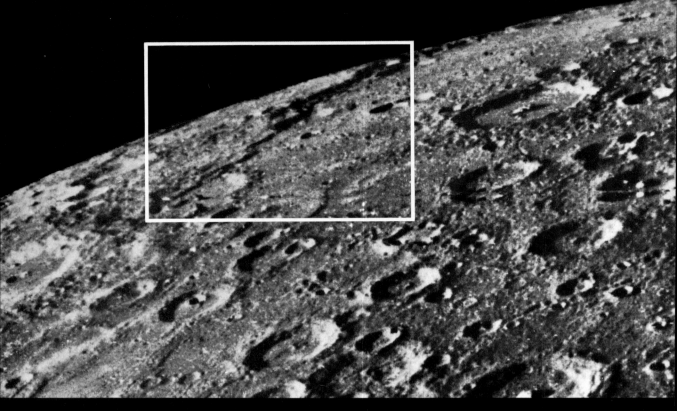

Scarps, or cliffs—revealed by cracks like the one that slashes across the area inside the white rectangle at top —tower some two miles high and snake for hundreds of miles through Mercury's cratered regions. Scientists think that the scarps are wrinkles formed some four billion years ago when the planet's core began to shrink.

Mercury's Kinship to Earth and Moon

Mariner X's first close-up photographs of Mercury produced an astonished double take among scientists. According to one exuberant astronomer, "Mercury is like the moon on the outside, but it may well be like the earth on the inside. For that reason, it's unique in the solar system." Like the moon, the surface of Mercury is pocked with craters and lava-filled basins. But Mariner also detected an earthlike magnetic field.

Scientists knew that planetary magnetism was produced by a "dynamo effect"—the rapid rotation of iron-cored planets like the earth. But Mercury rotates too slowly—once in every 58.6 earth days—for this effect to work. Now scientists postulate a large iron core that could produce magnetism in a slow rotating body.

The discovery of scarps buttressed the iron core theory; they were probably formed when the core cooled, making the surface crack.

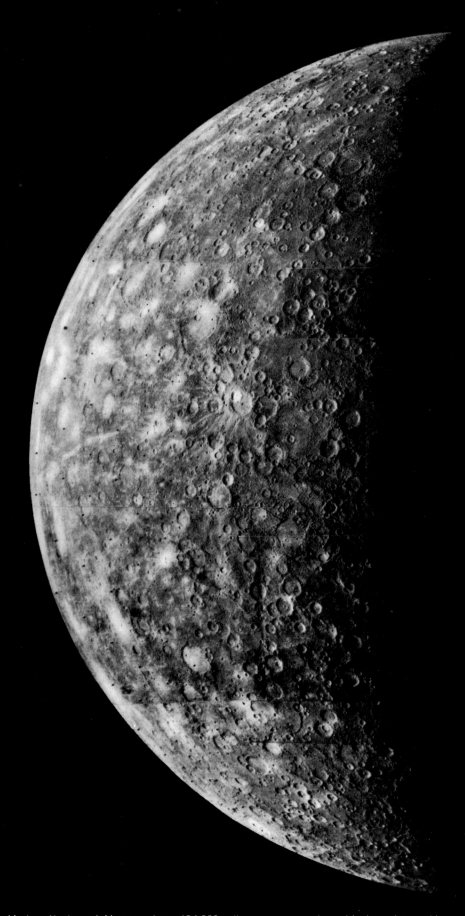

A sharp Mariner-X view of Mercury, from 124,000 miles away, reveals a bleak surface with moonlike craters and basins.

Teaching Animals to Talk

FROM CHIMPS AND SPARROWS COME CLUES TO LANGUAGE

by Don Moser

At ease in a comfortable Atlanta room, Lana approaches her typewriter and with the deft movements of a touch typist taps out a message: "Please machine give piece of apple." The computer that controls Lana's environment dispenses a slice of apple through a small slot in the wall of the room. Lana eats it, requests another. Then, apparently no longer hungry, she punches out a different message: "Please machine make window open." The shutter covering the window to the outside world immediately slides down. Lana moves over to the window and looks out at a pleasant vista of trees and grass.

In 30 seconds the omnipotent computer causes a little motor to hum, and the shutter closes again. Lana returns to her typewriter. Lonely, perhaps, she taps out a message to a friend in another room. "Please Tim move into room." The computer relays the message to Tim. He reads it and goes into the room, where Lana greets him with great affection.

To an observer Lana's behavior is astonishing. Not because she lives in a machine-controlled environment and communicates by sending messages through a godlike computer at Atlanta's Yerkes Primate Center, but because Lana is a four-year-old chimpanzee, and she seems to be learning to communicate with humans. Within the last year she has managed to increase her vocabulary from 25 to 73 words, has learned to identify eight colors, and without any special training has taught herself to carry on a rudimentary kind of conversation to get an object she particularly wants to have.

Experiments with Lana and other chimpanzees, which suggest that animals might learn to talk, are perhaps the most intriguing in a broad

Lana, a "talking" chimpanzee at Yerkes Primate Center, carries on a conversation with her trainer, Tim Gill, through signals flashed by computer. When she punches "?Tim tickle Lana" on the keyboard (top), Tim responds, "Yes." (center) and starts to tickle his happy ward (bottom).

spectrum of related studies. For a variety of purposes, this research seeks to penetrate the complex communications systems of the animal world, down to the very simplest forms of life. Animals send messages to one another with electrical pulses, flashing lights, postures, gestures, facial expressions, scents, color displays and a cacophony of clicks, stridulations, songs, barks, screams, grunts, whistles and purrs. Through all these methods they exchange useful information —enough information so that they can survive both as individuals and species.

Today behaviorists are working to decipher the meaning of this Tower of Babel; they are trying to learn just what animals say and how they say it, seeking not only to cast light on how animals communicate with one another, but also to discover the way humans learn to talk. Much of the work has been frustrating—the bright hopes of conversing with the friendly dolphin have now been dashed ("The Case of the Uncommunicative Dolphins," pages 160-161). But research with such unlikely creatures as two species of song sparrow has, oddly, revealed fascinating insights into the way humans learn to use language.

IS LANA LEARNING LANGUAGE?

It is the obvious and direct connection to language—long held to be one of the few attributes that unequivocally distinguishes man from all other animals—that makes the performance of chimpanzees like Lana so significant. There is no question that Lana spontaneously communicates with her human trainers. But the question may be asked, and in fact is being asked by skeptical scientists: Is Lana's performance on her giant keyboard simply the circus trick of an adept primate, or is she learning language? Some scientists answer: circus tricks. Unlike man, say the skeptics, Lana is merely being taught to manipulate symbols on a keyboard for rewards. Human beings apparently are born able to learn language, and what is more, they learn to use it automatically and compulsively; in a normal environment, an infant cannot be prevented from acquiring the ability to talk.

The gist of the argument centers around the definition of language. He who possesses language can deal with abstractions, with concepts and ideas, with things that are not physically present. He can describe past events or predict future events. The man who speaks one language can use it to learn another language. He can use language to discuss language itself, as in this sentence. It is this language-based ability to handle concepts and abstractions that supports man's great intellectual prowess.

Man's system of communication gives him one more distinction, albeit a dubious one: Alone among living creatures, he can lie. Most animals can communicate, but not with language; they do not conceptualize or make abstractions. Instead they broadcast information on a primal level: "I am hungry," or "I am frightened," or "I want sex." Indeed, when the dog, an old friend, looks into a man's eyes, his owner knows that his pet is speaking to him in its fashion, and he understands perfectly well what it is saying. But while the dog can communicate, it cannot talk. As Bertrand Russell once observed: "No matter how eloquently a dog may bark, he cannot tell you that his parents were poor but honest." Lana punches a computer so much more eloquently than a dog can bark that the question of whether or not she uses language may have to be settled by changing the definition of language.

It is not surprising that the most startling communications experiments so far have taken place with chimpanzees, for they are the creatures closest to man on the evolutionary ladder. However, the first attempts at coaxing chimpanzees to talk, beginning early in this century, were not very successful. In one of the more famous experiments during the 1940s, for instance, psychologists Keith and Cathy Hayes tried to teach English to a chimpanzee named Viki. But after years of intensive verbal instruction while Viki lived in the Hayes's home, all she could say was something that sounded like "mama," "papa," "cup" and "up."

No one knew why these experiments failed so miserably until the 1960s, when it became apparent that chimpanzees could never learn to speak, no matter how intelligent they were, because they lacked essential anatomical equipment for talking. Chimpanzees do not have a developed pharynx, the key part of the human vocal tract. In the last decade, however, scientists have developed a variety of nonverbal techniques in their attempt to bridge the species communication gap.

CONCEPTUALIZING WITH SIGN LANGUAGE

The first successful experiments were begun in 1966 by psychologists Allen and Beatrice Gardner when they began teaching a female chimpanzee named Washoe to use the American Sign Language—the hand language used by the deaf. Washoe, now being studied at the Institute for Primate Studies near Norman, Oklahoma, by psychologist Roger Fouts, has a vocabulary of 160 words. She uses sign language spontaneously, and, most significantly, seems to generalize and conceptualize frequently as if using language.

After being taught what the word "open" meant in relation to a door, Washoe generalized the idea and used the same word to request that any drawer or door be opened, or even that the water tap be turned on. Even more amazing was Washoe's grasp of the connection between a language symbol and her own species. She was raised in isolation, had never seen another chimpanzee and, moreover, had not been taught the word for chimpanzee. But when she was finally introduced to others of her kind, and found them repugnant, she applied to them a word she knew and apparently considered appropriate: "bugs." In a similar way, she extended the application of a word taught her for soiled objects or excrement. After a macaque monkey threatened her and she was asked the name of the animal, she signed "dirty monkey," and subsequently called her trainers dirty when they failed to fill her requests or otherwise annoyed her.

Lucy, another chimpanzee at Oklahoma's Institute for Primate Studies, displayed a similar capacity for generalization. Lucy was given a radish to eat before she was taught a sign for it, and when asked what it was, she tasted it and signed "cry hurt food," which is not a bad description by any standard. With equal plausibility, she called a watermelon "candy drink."

In a more complex—and demanding—test of chimpanzees' language ability, David Premack of the University of California at Santa Barbara employs another method of getting around the animals' crude vocalizing equipment. He uses visual symbols—three-dimensional chips of colored plastic in various shapes and sizes—to communicate with Sarah, another female chimp.

Sarah is an extraordinary pupil. She seems to comprehend conjunctions, plurals, the interrogative and even the conditional tense. She also seems to understand the concepts "same as" and "different from."

In one experiment Sarah was taught to recognize a plastic symbol as meaning "apple." Then she was shown a real apple and was given a set of words from which she had to select those describing the apple. She correctly selected the symbols for red as opposed to green, for round as opposed to square. Simple enough. But in the next test, Sarah was given the plastic symbol for apple—which happens to be flat, triangular and blue—and once again was asked to select the words that described it. Sarah chose the same descriptive word for the symbol that she had chosen to describe the real apple. The conclusion was inescapable: In her mind, the plastic symbol had come to stand for the real thing—just as the word does for English-speaking people.

The latest and technologically most complicated of the chimpanzee experiments are taking place with Lana at the Yerkes Regional Primate Research Center in Atlanta under the direction of Duane Rumbaugh, professor of psychology at Georgia State University. Lana's environment resembles a giant fishbowl: four walls of clear plastic, seven by seven feet. One wall contains a console with 75 buttons, each bearing a word or word group in "Yerkish," a language composed of geometrical symbols and named for the noted primatologist Robert Yerkes.

Above the console is a double row of screens that light up with symbols when Lana pushes the appropriate buttons. By observing the screens Lana can see what she is writing, just as a typist can check his performance by looking at the paper in the typewriter. The screens also light up when a technician in the adjacent room pushes his own set of buttons in order to "talk" to Lana.

Below the console are a number of dispenser

The Case of the Uncommunicative Dolphins

While most attempts to establish communication with animals have centered around chimpanzees, some researchers have felt that another animal had an even greater potential for learning human language—the bottle-nosed dolphin. These sleek, seagoing mammals have a unique appeal. Their visages are frozen into permanent Mona Lisa smiles and they have a finely developed sense of play. They are emotionally sensitive and very social. Several accounts describe their efforts to help drowning men to shore. In 1972, a pair of them saved a swimmer in the Indian Ocean off Mozambique by holding sharks at bay and pushing the tired woman to shore.

For researchers in communication, dolphins possess attributes of special significance. They are chatterboxes who issue an incessant stream of whistles, barks, clicks and Bronx cheers; they have large brains with an extremely precise sonar-like navigation device. They utter a series of high-pitched sounds as they travel and, by judging the ricocheting echoes, make fine judgments about the shape, size and distance of objects in the water around them.

In the 1950s neurophysiologist Dr. John Lilly became intrigued with the idea that the big brains of dolphins might reflect an intelligence of a human order. Lilly began working with dolphins to try to determine if there was more to their vocalizing than met the ear. He played back dolphin recordings at low speeds, and believed he heard the animals using words and phrases that were "verging so closely on humanlike . . . phonetic quality as to be eerie." He decided to teach them to speak in "humanoids."

Lilly's female research associate moved into a pool with a young male dolphin named Peter and stayed with him 24 hours a day for two and a half months. The experiment was difficult. For one thing, humans find it uncomfortable to be submerged in salt water, day in and day out; for another, young male dolphins take an exuberant sexual interest in almost anything, and their amorous advances are not easily repelled.

Whether or not these obstacles were to blame, the experiment was hardly a success. Lilly believed that Peter did learn to mimic a few humanoids, but progress was slight and the experiment was abandoned. Today the conception of the dolphin as a kind of linguistic parahuman has little support in scientific circles. "We must stop thinking of dolphins as little men in wetsuits," says David Caldwell of the University of Florida. Caldwell and his wife, Melba, among the leading delphinologists at work today, have spent years recording the sounds made by captive dolphins. As far as they can tell, dolphins, for all their vociferousness, do not say much—and certainly nothing that resembles human speech. "Fundamentally," says Melba Caldwell, "dolphin signals are variations on two statements—'Come close' or 'Go away.'"

"When we began our research," says David Caldwell, "people expected that a complete dictionary of words would soon be available for purchase alongside the French-English and German-English dictionaries in bookshops."

But the public at large did not take kindly to the Caldwells' findings. The scientists found themselves challenged by lecture audiences and reviled in letters. The Caldwells, who have enormous respect and affection for dolphins, are disturbed by this reaction but somewhat resigned to it. The couple will continue to study the animals, to learn more about man's seagoing friends. "Dolphins are not less important or less interesting creatures," says Melba Caldwell, "just because they don't talk."

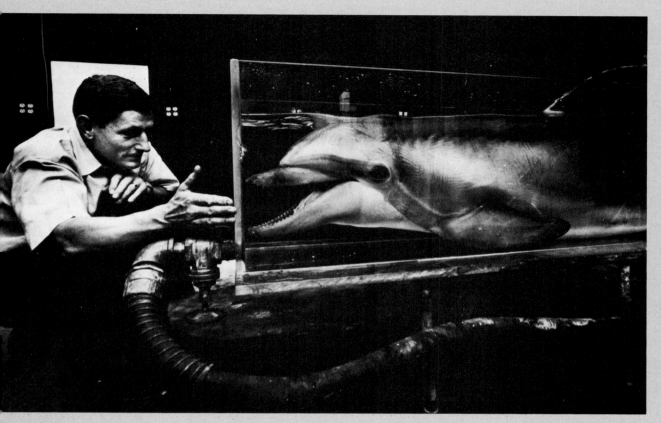

Neurophysiologist John Lilly (top) greets a three-year-old dolphin. During the 1960s, Lilly ran many fruitless experiments to teach dolphins to communicate with humans.

Dolphins do interact with pelicans, but how much communication goes on is questionable. Research indicates a common man-dolphin language may be unattainable.

slots that are connected to the computer. When Lana makes the correct request, motors hum and the machine responds immediately by passing out largesse. Lana can ask her machine for pieces of apple or banana, for M&M candies or drinks of water or soda pop. She can also ask the machine to open her window shutter so that she can see the trees and grass outside her plastic cube. Lana can request the computer to play tapes of rock and roll music, to show her slides or a movie, to dispense her ball, or to give her the blanket she likes to sleep with.

From time to time the words are shifted about on Lana's console to ensure that she is learning the symbols and not just memorizing a particular sequence of buttons. To receive a reward, she must first use correct Yerkish grammar—the machine will not grant her request if she punches "Please Lana machine M&M give," for example. And she must end each sentence by punching a period key that notifies the computer that the transmission is complete.

A SPONTANEOUS CONVERSATION

Lana has learned to observe these requirements of logic. More remarkably, she applies them with the flexibility that makes human language such a powerful tool. For example, while requesting a box of candy, Lana punched on her keyboard: "?Tim give Lana this can." She apparently asked for a can because she had not yet been taught the word for box. When Tim responded by giving Lana an empty can, the chimpanzee furiously punched: "? Tim give Lana name of this." "Box name of this." Tim signaled. Finally, Lana typed: "? Tim give Lana this box." and was given the box of sweets she had demanded so insistently —and logically.

Like the other language pupils, Lana, too, is beginning to conceptualize. Lana was taught the words "yes" and "no" in the context of a single question. She was shown an object and asked if a particular word was the name of the object. After two or three days of this kind of instruction, research assistant Tim Gill entered Lana's room, absent-mindedly took a piece of banana from her dispenser and popped it into his mouth. Lana immediately ran to the console and pressed the word "no" over and over again. Clearly Lana had achieved some concept of negativeness and was now able to apply it in a totally new context.

In small ways, Lana even seems to be seeking a kind of self-expression. Watching a requested movie with no one present, Lana will tell the computer, "? Movie name of this." just as a child might say to himself "cookie" and then eat it. Late at night Lana sometimes talks through the machine, putting words together in novel patterns, such as "? Lana carry shut foot chow." Meaningless prattle perhaps, but Tim Gill muses that she may be trying to practice her lessons.

An observer who sees Lana perform for the first time may begin to wonder whether the creature in the room is an ape or a small person with a furry pelt. Not long ago Tim Gill took a visitor to see Lana. When the two men entered the room adjacent to her plastic cube, she swung down from a bar attached to the machine and confronted the stranger with a quizzical expression. Then she swung back onto her bar, caromed off a plastic wall with such force that the room shook, and rebounded to her console. Her hand flashed out and she punched a rapid-fire sequence of buttons. The symbols for "Please Tim move into room." lighted up on the duplicate console in front of Tim's chair.

Tim punched "Yes" and went into Lana's plastic cube, where the two tussled playfully for a moment. Then Tim punched on the console, "? Tim groom Lana." Lana took in the lighted symbols at a glance and instantly punched "Yes." After a few minutes of grooming her fur, which Lana obviously enjoyed very much, Tim punched: "? Lana groom Tim." Lana quickly responded "Yes." and began to examine Tim's hand and arm, hunting for little bits of loose or broken skin and the parasites usually found in chimpanzee fur. A few minutes later Lana punched "Please Tim swing Lana." and was rewarded by being swung up to the ceiling. Then she asked for a tickle, and Tim grappled with her in a kind of rough-and-tumble wrestling match. Finally Tim punched on the console, "? Tim move out of room." For the first time Lana did not answer, and in fact paid no attention whatsoever to the lighted symbols in front of her.

Tim left, grinning. "She's spoiled. She didn't want me to leave, so she pretended not to see the question." As Tim continued to talk, Lana went to the console and punched out, "Please Tim move into room." Tim responded by pressing "No." Lana grew insistent, repeating the request again and again. After the sixth refusal from Tim, Lana abandoned Yerkish and reverted to basic chimp: She walked over to the plastic wall next to Tim, grimaced, and gave the partition a forceful kick.

The desire to talk to animals seems built into man's nature. It is a part of the fantasy literature that everyone grows up with—what man was ever so fortunate as Dr. Dolittle, who broke the code of animal language and could converse with pigs, ducks, owls and even giant moths? Many of the classics of children's literature—that is, those books people continue to enjoy long after they become adults—are about humans and animals talking together: *Alice in Wonderland, Winnie the Pooh, Charlotte's Web.*

BIRD SONG AND HUMAN SPEECH

But the lure of talking to animals is not necessarily what motivates scientists to devote tedious hours experimenting with animals' communications systems. Knowledge of those ways that animals get their message across to their trainers or to their fellow creatures can tell much about human language. Some of the lessons already learned from work with chimpanzees may be applied, for example, to the teaching of retarded children. But studies of other animals also provide useful clues to human abilities and disabilities. There are even surprising parallels between the manner in which birds learn to sing and the way humans learn to talk.

Peter Marler of Rockefeller University, working at his laboratory in Millbrook, New York, grew curious not long ago about the fact that male white-crowned sparrows, common birds of the Western United States, sang in regional dialects. After he reared some young white crowns in isolation, Marler found that they were unable to sing normally; the birds performed ineptly, producing whistles only vaguely approximating the white-crown song. However, if the isolated birds heard

recorded singing by wild white crowns, the experimental subjects got back on the track; they repeatedly sang accurate copies of the records.

Marler's birds were surprisingly choosy; they were willing to mimic only songs of their own species. If they heard another species' call, they were unimpressed, and sang as though they had never been trained at all. Marler concluded that the young sparrows were not genetically programed to sing their special call, but had to learn by listening to a white-crown adult song in order to sing properly.

Experiments by other researchers showed that if the young sparrows were deafened before they came into full voice, the songs they produced were a raspy buzz, more insect-like than bird-like. If the birds were exposed to adult song and given an opportunity to learn it, but were deafened before beginning to sing themselves, their attempts at song were just as hopeless. In other words, if the sparrow could not hear itself sing, then all the singing lessons were erased.

Moreover, in most cases the song-learning had to take place in the sparrow's infancy, before it was 50 days old. Thereafter, Marler found, the ability to learn to sing tailed off rapidly. (Apparently the same kind of mechanism applies to humans, who pick up foreign languages easily

At Rockefeller University's Field Research Center, Peter Marler adjusts an amplifier in a soundproofed sparrow cage. He hopes to discover if birds are born with the innate ability to sing or if they are taught by their parents and so find clues to the development of language in children.

when they are young, but tend to lose this facility as they grow older.)

Marler's experiments with another species of bird produced quite different results. Young male song sparrows, related to the white crowns, sang perfectly even when reared in isolation—though they, too, reverted to a sibilant buzz when they were deafened. The perplexing difference in the birds' behavior left Marler with an apparent anomaly: While each bird had to be able to hear its own voice in order to sing, one bird—the song sparrow—appeared to be genetically programed and did not need to learn its song from an adult; another—the white crown—seemed to have an instinctive sense of what its song should sound like, but it had to learn the subtleties of the tune from an adult of the species.

Marler resolved the anomaly by postulating an inborn "auditory template," a kind of model to be followed. Creatures, he believes, inherit a template that provides a model for communication behavior and perhaps for other behavior as well. They follow the template, practicing and modifying their behavior until it matches their inherited template. The template may be "closed" —that is, it can provide a very precise, detailed model, as it does in the song sparrows that sing correctly even in isolation. If the blueprint is "open," as it seems to be in white-crowned sparrows, it can simply offer general guidelines within which environmental influences affect behavior and make possible a considerable degree of individual variation—as with the regional dialects.

The sparrow studies, Marler believes, provide evidence to support the linguistic ideas of Noam Chomsky of M.I.T., who postulates that all known human languages, despite differences to the ear, have certain principles, or "deep structures," in common. These common principles, Chomsky believes, can be explained only by genetic influences; that is to say, humans must be genetically programed to talk. They may develop radically different languages, but all follow a broad blueprint that is innate.

Chomsky's belief in a human predisposition to language gets additional support from experiments reported in 1974 by researchers William Condon and Louis Sander of Boston University Medical Center. They found that infants ranging in age from 12 hours to 14 days moved their bodies in time with the rhythms of human speech, whether the language spoken was English or Chinese. The infants did not show any reaction to disconnected vowels or tapping noises. Condon and Sander concluded that the infants made fine distinctions between sounds in much the same way adults do—indicating a language perception that is operative from the first day of life. This natural gift enables infants to lay the groundwork for language long before they begin to speak.

The scientists who accept the possibility of deep language structures in human beings balk at accepting the possibility that animals will *ever* communicate with humans. Discovering any innate linguistic ability in chimpanzees, says Chomsky, "would certainly be a biological miracle. It would be the equivalent of discovering an animal with the capacity to fly that never thought of flying. If chimpanzees had the genetical ability to talk, they would have done so long ago."

APPLYING CHIMP LESSONS TO DEAF CHILDREN
But this pessimistic view of chimpanzees' linguistic prowess does not prevent the application of what has been learned from them to human affairs. Lana's mentor, Duane Rumbaugh, is planning a computerized training system like Lana's to be established at a Georgia center for retarded children. There a retarded child will be able to talk with other children, parents and teachers with the help of a special computer-derived language. Since the language system will be visual, it may also be useful in the early teaching of deaf children, who often have difficulty understanding that a language is there to be learned.

This approach is already paying dividends. Using the special plastic language aids that David Premack devised for Sarah, psychologists Patricia Hodges of California State College at Los Angeles and Ruth Deich at the Pacific State Hospital in Pomona, California, announced in September 1974 that they have successfully trained retarded children to construct simple sentences and to make abstractions. Such work suggests that whether or not a chimpanzee ever benefits from talking to people, people will.

One of many chimpanzees taught to communicate with humans, Lucy watches as psychologist Roger Fouts signals, "What do you want?" Because Lucy, like other chimps, lacks the vocal equipment of humans, she and her trainers communicate nonverbally. In this case, the mechanism is sign language, which she uses to request: "Roger tickle."

Summing Up the Year

A BRIEF REVIEW OF EVENTS, DISCOVERIES AND DEVELOPMENTS

ANTHROPOLOGY

The arrival of men in North America was pushed back even farther into the past, as were his migrations across the continent. And in Africa, studies of a present-day tribe called the !Kung indicated that a change from hunting to farming has caused, among other things, a drastic alteration in the status of women.

CULTURE SHOCK AMONG THE !KUNG

Among the most stable peoples in the world were a group of southern African tribesmen called the !Kung (the exclamation point indicates the sharp clicking sound made with the tongue when pronouncing the word). For more than 11,000 years, the !Kung had eked out a living as hunter-gatherers on the Kala-hari Desert, which sprawls across parts of Angola, Botswana and Southwest Africa. But during the last century, many of the !Kung have stopped hunting and gathering and begun farming. Reports by several anthropologists in 1974 indicate that the change of custom has set off culture shocks that are still being felt today.

Patricia Draper of the University of New Mexico wrote that the farming !Kung have become sexist. One reason is the women's loss of status as food gatherers; women contributed at least half the sustenance of the tribe and were as mobile as the male hunters. Now !Kung women care for children and cook, while the men leave their villages to prepare fields for crops and herd cattle.

Richard Lee of the University of Toronto found that the few nomadic !Kung left (less than 1,500 out of 30,000) even have different diets from their farming brethren. The nomads subsist on nuts, vegetables and meat—a balanced diet that keeps them slim and muscular. !Kung farmers eat mostly milk and grain, and are fatter and taller than the nomads.

Ultimately, the anthropologists' fieldwork could open doors to our own past: By studying the !Kungs' dramatic shift from hunter-gatherers to farmers—and the cultural upheaval that followed—they may be able to find clues to why man evolved into the kind of town- and city-dwelling animal he is today.

THE OLDEST AMERICAN

Only recently have many anthropologists accepted the idea that humans arrived in the New World as long as 25,000 years ago, crossing a land bridge that linked Siberia to Alaska during an ice age. Now two scientists claim that human bone fragments found in Southern California are nearly 50,000 years old—and could indicate human habitation of America even 100,000 years ago.

Jeffrey Bada and Roy Schroeder of the University of California and George Carter of Texas A&M revealed that a skull found in a sea cliff near Del Mar had been dated at 48,000 years, while a skull fragment discovered near La Jolla was found to be 44,000 years old. Both were dated by a technique, called racemization, developed in 1972 by Bada, an oceanographer *(Nature/Science Annual 1973, pages 80-81).*

The ancient bone samples had been in Southern California museums since the 1920s, but were examined by Bada at the insistence of Carter, a geography professor who has long maintained that man roamed the North American continent 100,000 years ago. If Bada's skull datings are accurate, Carter's theory may well be correct. The Bering Strait land bridge was exposed only during ice ages,

ONCE HUNTERS, !KUNG WOMEN ARE NOW CONFINED TO WASHING AND COOKING IN VILLAGES.

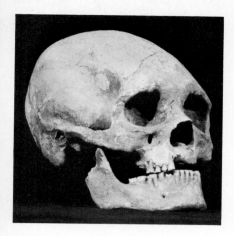

50,000-YEAR-OLD SKULL IS FOUND IN U.S.

was the oldest sign of habitation discovered in the East. The presence of an ice-age settlement in the East proves that the earliest Americans did not confine their travels to Alaska and the Western United States, as previously supposed, but like their much later Indian relatives, migrated throughout the continent, possibly following caribou and other game.

ARCHEOLOGY

Archeologists located a long-lost Civil War combatant, the Monitor, victor in the clash with the Confederate gunboat Merrimack in 1862. Studies of well-known relics revealed unknown facts about ice-age hunting and a kind of astronomy practiced by American Indians.

FINDING A CIVIL WAR BATTLESHIP

After 112 years, the remnants of the U.S.S. *Monitor,* the winner over the Confederacy's Merrimack in 1862 in the first naval battle between ironclad ships, was found and photographed. It was located in 220 feet of water some 15 miles south-

east of Cape Hatteras, North Carolina, where it had ignominiously sunk in a gale, while being towed, 10 months after its historic victory.

A number of expeditions had tried —and failed—to find the *Monitor.* Finally the Duke Marine Laboratory, using an 1857 coastal chart and the log of the ship that had been towing the *Monitor,* the U.S.S. *Rhode Island,* narrowed the search area to a rectangle five miles wide and 14 miles long. Then sonar, magnetic detectors, underwater television cameras and mechanical scoops located 22 wrecks in the search area. But only two had the *Monitor's* distinctive shape, and one of them turned out to be an old trawler with a semicircular wheelhouse.

Concentrating on the other, the scoops soon brought up some small pieces of yellow pine, the kind used on the *Monitor,* and anthracite coal, which fired the *Monitor's* steam engine. But the Duke team was not happy until an underwater television camera provided them a composite picture of the wreck, showing its distinctive stern, screw and turret.

The *Monitor* will be left where it is—it would probably come apart if an attempt were made to raise it and any salvaged parts would begin to decompose as soon as fresh air hit them.

when sea levels are lower. Thus man's ancestors, to have been in North America nearly 50,000 years ago, may well have crossed from Asia to Alaska during one of the previous ice ages, which occurred 70,000 and 140,000 years ago.

THE FIRST EASTERNERS

On a warm summer day in June 1973, an archeologist from the University of Pittsburgh accompanied his students on a field trip to Meadowcroft Village, a community of restored 19th Century homes near Pittsburgh. The work was meant simply as an exercise: the students were supposed to learn how to set up an archeological dig. Instead, James Adovasio and his untrained crew came up with one of the biggest scientific finds in decades: a treasure trove of ancient artifacts that since has led scientists to alter their theories about how Eastern North America was first settled.

Adovasio expected to find quite old relics of ancient Indians at the rocky, 300-square-yard site: animal and human bones, domesticated beans and broken tools dating perhaps to 10,000 years ago, the oldest Indian artifacts found in the Eastern United States. But in May 1974, after nearly a year of tests at the Smithsonian Institution in Washington, D.C., Adovasio was startled to learn that charcoal samples taken from a fire pit at Meadowcroft went back to the ice ages, 14,000 to 15,000 years ago. While signs of human settlement much older than this have been found in California *(above)* it

UNION SAILORS STAND GUARD ON THE MONITOR; SUNK IN 1862, IT WAS DISCOVERED IN 1974.

FROM THE ICE AGE: A BETTER SPEAR

How the ice-age inhabitants of North America were able to kill 12-foot-tall mammoths—in such numbers that the slaughter has been blamed for wiping out the animals—has long amazed the experts. In October, Larry Lahren of the University of Calgary and Robson Bonnichsen, who is with the National Museum of Man in Ottawa, found a possible explanation in the carved bone implements, long known to archeologists but ignored, that have been discovered scattered across much of North America.

At a burial site near Wilsal, Montana, the archeologists found the remains of several of these artifacts. When reassembled, the bones seemed to be carved in such a way that they could fit snugly onto the end of spears. Thus, the scientists concluded that early North Americans fabricated bone foreshafts with stone tools, attached them to the wooden spear shafts and then fitted the foreshafts with flint spear points. The bone foreshaft was a great aid to ice-age hunters, as it added strength and resiliency to the spear's thrusting point, enabling the entire shaft to penetrate deeper into the animal without breaking.

Lahren and Bonnichsen believe the foreshafts had a more sophisticated use: They could have been constructed so a hunter could pull the wooden shaft from a mammoth's body and instantly replace the spear with a new foreshaft-spear point, providing a weapon with refills.

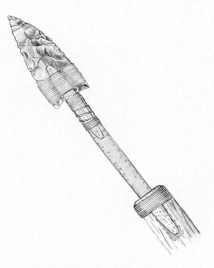

DID BONE SHAFTS KILL MAMMOTHS?

AN INDIAN OBSERVATORY

The strange pattern of rocks had long puzzled archeologists. The stones are laid out on a remote shoulder high on

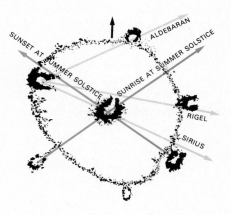

THIS MONUMENT ALIGNS STONES AND STARS.

Medicine Mountain in Wyoming's Big Horn range, forming a lopsided circle some 27 yards across. In the center lies a mound, or cairn, from which 28 lines radiate like the spokes of a wagon wheel. Six smaller cairns are located on or near the rim of the wheel.

Local Indian lore offers no explanation for the wheel, but it was generally believed to have been a site for religious ceremonies. In early June, however, John Eddy, a solar physicist at the National Center for Atmospheric Research in Boulder, Colorado, reported that the wheel was in fact a primitive observatory —used by Western Indians to mark the seasons, like Stonehenge in England and "woodhenge" at the pre-Columbian Indian metropolis of Cahokia *(Nature/Science Annual 1974, Indian City on the Mississippi, pages 125-139)*.

Eddy found that a line drawn between the center cairn and another one on the rim of the stone circle pointed directly to the place on the horizon where the sun came up on the morning of the summer solstice. Other sightings with different cairns provided alignments with one bright star (Aldebaran) at dawn just before the solstice sunrise; with another (Rigel) one lunar month later, and a third (Sirius) two lunar months after the solstice. He also found a set of cairns that lined up with the point on the horizon

where the sun set on the evening of the solstice. The spokes, he concluded, were probably used as a calendar, dividing the lunar month into 28 days.

Eddy speculated that the wheel could have been built by any of the tribes that dwelt in the area—the Cheyenne, Crow, Sioux, Arapaho or Shoshone—sometime around 1760, an estimate based on radiocarbon dating of wood found in one of the cairns. That was well before they had much contact with Europeans who might have taught them astronomy.

ASTRONOMY

A supposedly star-bright comet fizzled —although astronomers greatly expanded their knowledge of comets by studying the body; a Russian-born psychiatrist's bizarre theory of a giant comet nearly colliding with earth was successfully scuttled; meanwhile, aerospace researchers revealed how close earth had come to a real cosmic catastrophe. Scientists also launched proposals suggesting that life on earth was originally delivered by meteors, and began using the most distant stellar objects in the known universe to predict earthquakes.

BRIGHT NEWS FROM A WAN COMET

Professional and amateur astronomers all over the world got set to view the spectacular show promised by Kohoutek —heralded as the comet of the century. The show bombed. All through Kohoutek's swing by earth, which was most visible in January 1974, the comet for some reason turned out to be less dusty than expected and thus did not reflect enough sunlight to glow with the expected brightness.

Kohoutek may have been a visual flop, but it was a smash hit with instrument-equipped astronomers, providing them much new data on the structure, origin and behavior of comets. Two Canadian chemists, Gerhard Herzberg and Hin Lew, noticed that the emissions from the comet's tail matched those of steam that had been ionized, or broken into electrically charged atomic groups. Thus,

Kohoutek's tail appears to contain water vapor, supporting the theory that comets are huge chunks of ice, melted and ionized as they brush by the sun.

Radio telescopes provided an even more startling discovery: Kohoutek was emitting radio waves. They came, scientists found, from two kinds of molecules, methyl cyanide and hydrogen cyanide, in the comet's head. Since both of these molecules have been found in dust and gas clouds in the Milky Way, their presence in Kohoutek seems to support recent theories that comets were formed of the same material from which the solar system was born.

A NEAR MISS FOR EARTH

On August 10, 1972, one of the brightest fireballs ever seen streaked northward across the afternoon skies of Montana, Utah, Idaho and the Canadian province of Alberta, producing sonic booms and dazzling thousands of onlookers, many of whom were able to photograph it. Unknown to them, the fiery visitor had also been observed by a U.S. Air Force satellite, which recorded its trajectory and other data. But it was not until 1974 that five aerospace scientists in California revealed that the spectacle narrowly missed turning into a major disaster.

Using data from the satellite, the scientists estimated that the meteor was about 13 feet across, weighed 1,100 tons and had sliced through the earth's atmosphere at about 33,000 miles per hour before heading back into space. At its nearest approach to the earth, above the Idaho-Montana border, it was only 36 miles high. Had the meteor hit the earth, said the scientists, the impact would have rivaled the explosive force of the atomic bombs that leveled Hiroshima and Nagasaki during World War II.

A METEORIC START FOR LIFE

Did life begin on earth or did it arrive from outer space by natural—or artificial—means? Science fiction writers, and some scientists, have speculated that an extraterrestrial civilization might have delivered the "seeds" of life to earth billions of years ago. Others have suggested that chemical precursors of life were transported to earth on meteors *(Nature/ Science Annual 1974, pages 98-111)*. In mid-January, scientists Keith Kvenvolden of NASA's Ames Research Center and George Yuen of the University of Arizona backed meteors as the means of delivery. They announced that in fragments recovered from two meteorites they had found 17 varieties of fatty acids, substances that are used by earthly plants and animals to produce more complex biological molecules.

The meteorites that contained these essential-to-life molecules were part of the dozens of tons of meteoric material that strike the earth's outer atmosphere every day. Indeed, when the solar system was younger and more cluttered with debris, the meteoric bombardment was undoubtedly heavier, and more meteors survived the trip through the atmosphere to hit the earth. Because a ton of meteoric material would yield about a half pound of fatty acids, Kvenvolden reasons, there must have once been plenty of organic matter lying on the surface of the young earth. He says that this plentiful matter "may have contributed directly to the origin of life on earth."

A WILD THEORY DISPROVED

It was not until February 1974 that Velikovsky's peers finally brought him to earth. It took scientists 24 years to get around to it, but during the 1974 meeting of the American Association for the Advancement of Science in San Francisco, the outlandish theory of early earth history proposed by psychiatrist Immanuel Velikovsky was finally attacked head-on by more conventional experts.

In his book *Worlds in Collision,* published in 1950, Velikovsky claimed that a large comet broke away from Jupiter in 1500 B.C. and, brushing repeatedly past the earth, caused a series of catastrophes recorded in the Bible.

Among the results of this cosmic near-collision were the parting of the Red Sea, the plagues and flies, rivers running with blood and manna from heaven (which Velikovsky said consisted of carbohydrates from the comet's tail). In this bizarre scenario, the comet then jolted Mars out of its orbit, sending it close to the earth in 800 B.C. and causing more catastrophes. Eventually Mars returned to its present orbit and the comet moved into a stable path of its own, becoming the planet Venus.

At the AAAS meeting, scientists allowed Velikovsky to present his theories —and then dispassionately demolished them, to the satisfaction of all but the most rabid of Velikovsky's followers.

Velikovsky was disputed first by AAAS panelist Peter Huber, professor of ancient history at Zurich's Federal Institute of Technology, who displayed photographs of tablets and other ancient records that showed Venus in the sky as early as 3000 B.C.—1,500 years before Velikovsky said that it had been born. The *coup de grâce* was delivered by astronomer Carl Sagan of Cornell University, who pointed out that any event that could have ejected a Venus-sized comet from Jupiter would have completely melted the planet. Moreover, even assuming that this cataclysm was possible, to have rained enough manna to feed the wandering Jews for 40 years, the comet would have had to have a mass at least equal to Jupiter's. Velikovsky's contention that the flies that fell from the comet onto Egypt were indistinguishable from terrestrial organisms, Sagan added, is a "gross absurdity," since the insects would surely have burned up in their plunge through the atmosphere.

PREDICTING QUAKES WITH A QUASAR

Geophysicists have come to believe in the last decade that, by accurately measuring minute earth movements preceding earthquakes, they can predict when and where a quake will strike. Since January 1974 scientists working at the Jet Propulsion Laboratory in Pasadena, California, have been using one of astronomy's newest—as well as most bizarre—techniques to do just this. The new tool is a quasar, one of the huge, stellar-like bodies at the edge of the universe that emit powerful radio waves.

Utilizing such a gigantic, distant tool is necessary precisely because an earthquake's pretremor movements are so subtle. The ground swell preceding a major earthquake may stretch for hundreds of square miles, but only a few inches to a few feet in height. Measurement of such small effects by ordinary instruments is extremely difficult and very costly, and it is complicated by mountains or even smog that interfere with normal surveying techniques.

Quasar measurement neatly sidesteps these problems. JPL scientists began their experiment by tuning in on a quasar with two radio antennas: a movable one in Pasadena and a fixed one 125 miles away at Goldstone in the Mojave Desert. The antennas straddle the San Andreas Fault, California's major earthquake zone. Because the antennas were separated, radio waves from the quasar struck one antenna a few 10 billionths of a second before it reached the other.

After measuring the difference in the signal's arrival time with atomic clocks, the information was fed into computers, which computed the distance between the antennas and their elevations with an accuracy of an inch or less. Any change in the quasar-measured distance between antennas or their elevation indicates that the earth has moved, and the amount of change tells precisely how much it has moved.

The JPL team plans to record radio signals from 20 different quasars on points surrounding the San Andreas Fault with their movable antenna. The numerous quasar recordings will tell the scientists where the earth has moved and enable them to predict small quakes —which occur about three days after initial swells. Such readings could also indicate massive upheavals as much as three years in the future.

BEHAVIOR

New techniques allowed scientists to read emotions in facial expressions, decipher brain waves and regulate brain activity, while an old technique—statistics—testified to the affluent life style of most Americans. A highly touted parapsychology experiment, like so many in that disputed science, was a fake but another won some scientific endorsement.

READING EMOTIONS IN A FACE

Even the most emotionless poker face contains clues about the feelings of its owner—in the form of tiny electrical impulses around the facial muscles. And psychologist Gary Schwartz of Harvard now says he has found a way to detect these clues and thus determine a person's real emotions.

Schwartz attached pairs of electrodes to volunteers' skin above each of four facial muscles. First he asked the subjects to think about sad, joyful and enraging experiences, and recorded their reactions on an oscilloscope. Then he requested that his subjects express the same emotions—but without consciously altering their features. By using the recorded conscious emotional responses as a base, Schwartz was able to accurately trace emotions even when the subjects' expressions were blank.

RUNNING A COMPUTER BY THOUGHT

A computer was hooked to the human brain by Lawrence Pinneo of Stanford Research Institute, who programed it to take orders directly from the subject's thoughts. Pinneo started with 25 subjects, each fitted with an electrode-studded helmet. The electrodes were connected to an electroencephalograph (a machine that records brain waves).

The subjects were asked to think but not to articulate seven different commands: up, down, left, right, slow, fast and stop. The brain-wave patterns from these commands were then fed into a computer that had been programed to recognize the patterns. If the computer detected the pattern for "down," for example, it would move a spot of light toward the bottom of a television screen. If it discerned the pattern for "slow," it would slow the motion of the dot. Each subject, thinking at random of any of the seven commands, was capable of moving the computer-directed dot of light around the TV screen—literally at will —making it respond correctly about 60 per cent of the time.

Pinneo is convinced that the accuracy of the computer's recognition of brain

waves can be greatly improved. He foresees the time when the pilot of a high-speed aircraft, too occupied to scan the complex bank of instruments for a correct reading, will merely have to think "rate of climb" or "compass heading." The computer will immediately flash on a large display board in front of the pilot the correct number of feet per minute or degrees away from north.

THE MENTAL PACEMAKER

José Delgado of the Autonomous University of Madrid, noted for his experiments in controlling the brain through the use of electrical stimulation *(Nature/ Science Annual 1971, page 170),* told a Manhattan symposium that he was developing a "mental pacemaker" that may someday regulate brain activity in much the same way that a conventional pacemaker stabilizes the heart. Delgado has already shown that electrodes in the brains of cats and monkeys can produce changes in their behavior. Working with humans, he has been able to evoke such feelings as pain, fear and pleasure.

The current version of the pacemaker has been used to help an accident victim who was in such continuous pain that he begged doctors to amputate his arm. Instead, Delgado inserted electrodes in the pain center of the victim's brain; for one hour daily they were alternately activated and deactivated every five seconds. The pain gradually lessened and finally disappeared after three months.

Eventually Delgado hopes to develop an automatic pacemaker that might allow epileptics to go about their business without worrying about having a seizure. Whenever the epileptic's brain waves indicated that he was about to have an attack, his pacemaker would alert the minicomputer implanted in his body to activate electrodes in his brain and prevent the attack—without the patient knowing that he had had a close call.

A HARD LOOK AT AMERICANS

The United States government took a first step toward establishing statistical indexes of nationwide social well-being —comparable to the economic indicators used in policy-making—with the publication in February of *Social Indicators, 1973*. The 272-page volume is a compilation of data on everything from health and education to leisure. Among the trends reported:

● The average length of life for persons born in the United States increased from 49.3 years in 1900 to 71.1 years in 1971. Women live for 74.9 years on the average, men 67.4 years.

● Between 1949 and 1972, the ranks of the college educated swelled from 5.8 to 19 per cent in the 25 to 29 age group.

● Despite efforts to improve mass transit, 87 per cent of all workers traveled to work by automobile in 1970, compared to 82 per cent in 1963.

● The percentage of Americans living in "substandard" dwellings declined from 48.6 per cent in 1940 to a low of 7.4 per cent in 1970.

● More than three quarters of the national wealth is controlled by the top 20 per cent of American families. The bottom 20 per cent of the population has only 1 per cent of the wealth.

● The percentage of households owning television sets rose from 9 per cent in 1950 to 96 per cent in 1972.

A PSYCHIC FAKE UNCOVERED

Another of the frauds that for almost a century have plagued research in parapsychology, or psychic phenomena, was uncovered in August *(ESP, Nature/Science Annual 1974, pages 96-97)*. Walter Levy, the bright, newly appointed director of the Institute for Parapsychology in Durham, North Carolina, resigned under fire for faking an experiment indicating that animals have the ability to influence events in the future.

While a protégé of parapsychologist J. B. Rhine, who founded the institute and pioneered research in extrasensory perception (ESP) in the 1930s, Levy had computerized ESP research.

In the experiment that was to prove his downfall, he had implanted electrodes in the pleasure zones of rats' brains, and arranged a system that, if unaffected by outside influences, would

deliver electrical pulses to stimulate the pleasure zones 50 per cent of the time. But if the rats could affect the system by sheer will power (psychokinesis), they could make it deliver pleasurable impulses more often than not.

Levy was soon reporting 54 per cent scores, suggesting that rats indeed had psychic powers. But he was seen tampering with a recorder, and was found out. When confronted with this evidence of cheating, he confessed, claiming— as did researcher William Summerlin in the Sloan-Kettering mouse scandal *(Biochemistry, below)*—that he had been under great pressure at the institute to produce positive results.

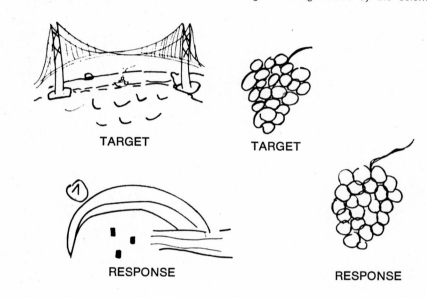

TARGET   TARGET

RESPONSE   RESPONSE

A PSYCHIC READS THOUGHTS OF TARGET DRAWINGS TO MAKE RESPONSE SKETCHES.

AND ANOTHER PSYCHIC VINDICATED?

While one psychic phenomenon was debunked *(above)* others were defended. Uri Geller, who claims extrasensory powers, had also been branded a fraud by many in the scientific community. But in October, the prestigious and conservative British journal *Nature* reported that physicists Harold Puthoff and Russell Targ of the Stanford Research Institute had experimentally tested Geller's psychic ability and, in the words of the scientists, found that he could send and receive information by an "as yet unidentified perceptual modality." The scientists consulted professional magicians in

order to design a "cheat-proof" test for Geller. What they came up with would have challenged Houdini. Geller was sealed in a room whose metal walls blocked all outside influences, including radio waves. Via an intercom, Geller told the physicists he was ready. The scientists, who were stationed in a room down the hall, randomly scanned dictionaries, picked the first word they felt could be graphically depicted, and then drew a picture of it as a target for Geller's sense. Geller, locked in his cell, responded by trying to reproduce the drawing.

He turned in 10 sets of "response" sketches; all showed a similarity to the target drawings made by the scientists, and some—like those reproduced here —were remarkably similar.

Although Puthoff and Targ concluded that Geller possessed some inexplicable powers, they did not confirm all his claims—he maintains he can bend nails with his mind. Many scientists remain skeptical; the report in *Nature* was published over the objection of experts who felt the experiments were flawed.

BIOCHEMISTRY

In an unusual move, scientists shelved certain experiments in genetics after discovering that their work could be dan-

gerous to man. A pharmacologist report-ed isolating a substance in the brains of goldfish believed responsible for mem-ory. However, a widely heralded break-through in immunology—the grafting of skin from humans onto mice and the im-plantation of human corneas in rabbits —was discredited.

RED LIGHT ON GENETIC TINKERING

Genetic engineering, the manipulation of hereditary characteristics, moved closer to reality in April—and by August took a step backward after a string of quick suc-cesses frightened scientists. Afraid that their work might prove dangerous to mankind, the researchers declared an unprecedented moratorium on certain at-tempts to tinker with genes.

The strange sequence of events be-gan after Annie Chang and Stanley Cohen of Stanford reported that they had transplanted genes, the units of heredity, from Staphylococcus bacteria into com-pletely unrelated bacteria, *Escherichia coli,* to produce hybrids that had genetic characteristics of both species. In May, the Stanford researchers, working with John Morrow, of the Carnegie Institution, presented more remarkable news: they had incorporated genes from a South Af-rican toad into *E. coli* bacteria. When the altered bacteria reproduced, their off-spring contained the animal genes.

At the same time, Cohen's group was proceeding with a project designed to produce practical results: transplanting into *E. coli* bacteria the genes that pro-duce the antibiotic called streptomycin. Because *E. coli* are easier to cultivate than the bacteria that produce strepto-mycin naturally, production of the anti-biotic could thus be expedited. The sky seemed the limit for gene transplanters.

In July, however, 11 prominent mo-lecular biologists—including Cohen—is-sued a grim note of caution. In a letter published both in the influential Brit-ish journal *Nature* and the American journal *Science,* they appealed to their colleagues throughout the world to ob-serve a temporary ban on experiments that might inadvertently convert relative-ly harmless bacteria like *E. coli* (whose natural habitat is the human colon) into killer bugs that could infect humans around the world. The statement called for a voluntary ban on two kinds of experiments—transplanting into bacteria 1) genes that would give them resistance to drugs, and 2) genes from cancer-causing or other kinds of virus. The bi-ologists also noted that the insertion of any animal genes into bacteria should "not be undertaken lightly," since many types of animal cells contain genes com-mon to certain tumor viruses.

The proposed ban, which was quickly endorsed by the National Academy of Science, seemed to win approval from scientists. They agreed to hold back on potentially dangerous gene-transplanting experiments until February 1975, when an international conference of molecular biologists will attempt to make a better assessment of the possible risks.

THE TRANSPLANT SCANDAL

Fakery is rare in scientific research sim-ply because it is quickly detected by other scientists who try to duplicate the fraudulent work. That self-policing sys-tem worked once again in April, when astounding results at New York's pres-tigious Sloan-Kettering Institute for Can-cer Research were revealed to be as phony as a circus dog-faced boy.

The work began, honestly enough, in 1970, when Stanford University research-er William Summerlin discovered what seemed to be a way of circumventing the immune-system reaction: the process that causes human and animal bodies to reject foreign substances, including transplanted tissue and organs. Moving on to the University of Minnesota and in 1973 to Sloan-Kettering, Summerlin re-ported an even more startling break-through: the successful transplanting of skin from one strain of mice to other, ge-netically dissimilar mice, the grafting of skin from humans, guinea pigs and pigs onto mice, and the implantation of hu-man corneas in rabbits.

In April, Summerlin's dizzying career came to an abrupt halt. He was accused by his colleagues of faking his results. His claims of success had been based on a technique in which he kept tissue to be transplanted in laboratory cultures for several weeks. That process, he sug-gested, somehow washed off the proteins that enable the body to distinguish for-eign material from its own cells, making the foreign tissue appear harmless to the immune-reaction system. But other re-searchers could not duplicate his results. Then in March, after Summerlin had dis-played several mice with "successful" skin grafts from different strains of mice, other S.K.I. researchers examined the mice and found that the dark, grafted skin on two animals could be washed off with alcohol. Confronted with the evi-dence, Summerlin immediately admitted that he had inked the "grafts" with a felt-tipped pen. A special investigating com-mittee at Sloan-Kettering cast doubt on much of his earlier work, and ordered his immediate discharge.

DEMOGRAPHY

While many nations struggled with spi-raling populations, the growth rate of the United States continued to level off. But its composition might alter; if American women could control the sex of their offspring, a survey found, the popula-tion would at the outset be weighted heavily toward males.

A 28-YEAR LOW IN U.S. BIRTHS

Explosive population growth still plagues many areas of the world, but the United States seems well on its way toward ef-fective control. There were 3,141,000 births in the United States in 1973, the smallest number for any year since 1945. More significantly, the fertility rate for 1973 dropped to 69.3 births per 1,000 women, the lowest figure recorded since records were begun in 1910.

After these statistics were analyzed, the Census Bureau's National Center for Health Statistics reported in April that for the second year in a row the total fertility rate of the United States had dropped below the figure necessary to maintain population at a steady level.

Even so, the population will continue to increase well into the next century, a Center spokesman explained, because women of childbearing age still constitute a larger-than-normal proportion of the population. The reason is that children born in the post-World War II baby boom are currently of childbearing age. Thus, despite record lows in fertility and birth rates, the population of the United States grew in 1973 by 1,164,000. And not until the first half of the 21st Century could the present trend bring the United States to the stage that many environmentalists consider necessary if man is to survive: zero population growth.

Not everyone agrees with that goal, however. At the first intergovernmental conference on population in Bucharest in August, a different view was heard.

A Chinese delegate said worries over population increases were groundless, and an Indian representative declared: "They shout and scream about 'standing room only.' But we believe in reincarnation, my friend, so don't worry. You'll be back." Even the host country, Romania, blasted efforts at population control, asserting that the Communist nation was determined to increase its population 25 per cent by 1980. As for the 1.5 billion people already suffering from hunger, said Romanian President Nicolae Ceausescu, science would provide.

A DELICATE BIRTH BALANCE

For every 100 girls born in the United States, on the average, 105 boys are born —a ratio that stays remarkably constant over the years. But what would that ratio be if parents could somehow select the sex of their offspring? In the long run, concluded two population experts after a mass survey of married and formerly married women, not much different.

As part of the government's National Fertility study, 5,981 married women under the age of 45 were asked questions about their preference for the sex of any children that they might have in the future. Analyzing the answers, sociologist Charles Westoff of Princeton and Ronald Rindfuss of the University of Wisconsin determined that if sex selection were readily available and widely used, there would be a temporary "20 per cent excess of male births," bringing the ratio of male babies to female babies to 124

to 100. This jump in male births would occur because most women who have not yet had a baby would prefer a boy first—by nearly a 2-to-1 ratio.

If this emphasis on boys continued, it would produce a serious sex imbalance. However the researchers found that most women, after having a first, male baby, would select a girl as their second child. As a result, the sex ratio would eventually balance out at about 110 boy infants to every 100 girls.

DRUGS

The idea that marijuana increases sexual potency was successfully scuttled by researchers. There was more bad news in the drug field. Scientists linked heart disease to a substance found in cigarette smoke, compiled more evidence that alcoholism causes liver disorders, and found that an imported rejuvenating pill favored by Chinese-Americans harms rather than cures.

POT—SEXUAL STIMULANT?

Many marijuana users believe that smoking pot improves their sex lives. That folk wisdom went up in smoke in 1974. A team including famous sex researcher William Masters reported that marijuana apparently not only reduces the production of male sex hormones but also impairs the fertility and potency of males.

The researchers compared 20 men, 18 to 28 years old, selected from a group of volunteers who had smoked marijuana at least four days a week for a minimum of six months, with another 20 men of similar ages who had never smoked marijuana. On the average, the pot smokers had levels of the male hormone, testosterone, 44 per cent lower than the nonsmokers. More than a third of the marijuana smokers also had diminished sperm counts; some of them were sterile.

Furthermore, the testosterone levels and sperm counts were correspondingly lower among more frequent pot users. Two of them were impotent—apparently, said the report, "in association with marijuana use." One regained his potency

several weeks after he stopped smoking. The conclusion drawn by Dr. Masters: "It now appears possible that there may be severe consequences of frequent, intensive use of the drug."

SMOKING AND DISEASE

There was more bad news for smokers in 1974. Dr. Poul Astrup of the Rigshospitalet in Copenhagen and Dr. Wilbert Aronow of the University of California College of Medicine implicated carbon monoxide, rather than nicotine, as the ingredient of cigarette smoke that produces the high incidence of heart disease among smokers. They exposed experimental animals to heavy concentrations of carbon monoxide for several months, and found changes in their arterial walls that were "indistinguishable" from circulatory ailments in humans. Their findings indicate, among other things, that filters—which do not block carbon monoxide—will not help smokers ward off the damaging effects of cigarettes on the cardiovascular system.

In March, Aronow and two University of California colleagues reported that carbon monoxide also aggravates the calf pains that afflict patients with arterial disease after moderate exercise. In experiments with 10 volunteers, Aronow found that the pains developed 17 per cent sooner, on the average, when those in the test group were exposed to carbon monoxide before exercising.

In addition, two Australian researchers reported that smoking seriously depresses immunity to disease. Exposing both mice and cultures of human and animal cells to cigarette smoke, microbiologists David Keast and Patrick Holt found that substantial portions of disease-fighting cells were weakened or even destroyed.

After 42 weeks of smoking, the capacity of the mice to make such cells was sharply reduced. That weakening of the immune system could account for the high incidence among smokers of chronic bronchitis, recurring respiratory infections and cancer. There was one bright note. Keast, Holt and W. R. Thomas reported that 16 weeks after their test animals were taken off their smoking regimen, immunity partially returned.

THE DRINKING MAN'S LIVER

One of the more familiar axioms of medicine is the belief that alcoholics develop cirrhosis and other diseases of the liver not from drink but from a poor diet. In January, two New York City doctors released a report on a four-year study of alcohol-consuming baboons that seems to disprove the old theory.

Emanuel Rubin of the Mount Sinai School of Medicine and Charles Lieber of the Bronx Veterans Hospital fed one group of 13 baboons a high-vitamin, high-protein diet, including enough alcohol to provide half the daily caloric intake. Another group of 13 was given the same daily amount of vitamins, protein and calories, but no alcohol. All the baboons on the alcoholic diet suffered liver damage; among the abstaining baboons there was no liver disease. Commented Rubin: "You cannot protect yourself against alcoholic damage by eating well; what counts is the total amount of alcohol you drink."

DANGER FROM AN OLD REMEDY

Black and foul-smelling, the Nan Lien ginseng rejuvenating pill was a longtime favorite in San Francisco's Chinatown. When gulped down with a glass of water, the pill brought instant relief from various aches and pains. But in June, the U.S. Food and Drug Administration announced that in addition to the pill's 58 listed and harmless ingredients, rhinoceros horn, silkworm, male mouse droppings, there was an unlisted and hazardous one, phenylbutazone. Just as the FDA was removing the Nan Lien pills from the market, one user died.

Phenylbutazone, a drug developed in Western laboratories, is an effective anti-inflammatory agent. Makers of ginseng medicines in Taiwan had apparently spiked their pills with the drug so that consumers would attribute their fast relief from pain to the mystical power of Eastern potions. But even when phenylbutazone is taken in properly prescribed doses, it can have serious side effects. From 1 to 10 out of every 1,000 patients who take the drug, for example, come

down with agranulocytosis, a rare malady that hampers the body's ability to produce white blood cells and leaves victims susceptible to infectious diseases.

Because of all the publicity about the ginseng pills, they quickly disappeared from the shelves of stores in the Bay area's Chinese communities. The FDA soon after alerted customs officials to seize any ginseng products flowing into the United States. Just two days after this alert the first pill victim was dead.

ENERGY

While a debate over the safety of nuclear power increased, a highly touted experiment to use atomic explosions to release natural gas trapped underground proved a dud. There was good news for the consumer, however: A British inventor claimed that by mixing oil with water fuel consumption in home furnaces could be sharply reduced.

SAFE NUCLEAR POWER

From the day the idea was proposed, electric generating plants powered by nuclear energy have been attacked as dangerous; critics pointed out that they might leak radioactivity into the environment, causing radiation sickness or even death over broad areas. A 3,300-page M.I.T. report released in August, however, draws just the opposite conclusion: that nuclear power is, if anything, safer than any other energy source currently being used for domestic purposes.

The two-year and three-million-dollar study directed by M.I.T. nuclear engineer Norman Rasmussen was underwritten by the Atomic Energy Commission, hardly an unbiased sponsor; nonetheless, the study was quite rigorous and included scientists from private universities as well as from the AEC.

Dozens of real and hypothetical accidents were postulated and analyzed, as were the probabilities that they would occur in nuclear power plants. The figures were then compared with nonnuclear accidents like floods, hurricanes and air crashes. Rasmussen and his colleagues

found that there was an infinitesimally small probability—one in a million per year—of a major reactor accident causing 1,000 fatalities or more when 100 plants were in operation. By contrast, the chances of an equal loss of life by fire was 1,000 times greater, the chances by earthquake were 20,000 times greater and 40,000 times greater by hurricane. Loss of property in the $100 million range, the study estimated, would occur only once every five centuries, whereas similar loss by fire would be expected to occur every two years.

The findings, however, did little to still critics. Two Washington, D.C., scientists—Arthur Tamplin and Thomas Cochran—argued that the report was meaningless since it excluded other potential sources of accident: sabotage and spills from storage facilities. They charged at the same time that the entire study was suspect because it confirmed AEC attitudes about nuclear power plants. And a spokesman for consumer advocate Ralph Nader pointed out that an essential safety mechanism—the emergency cooling system that keeps the active core from melting and spewing out radiation—has yet to be tested.

NUCLEAR BLAST FOR GAS: A FIZZLE

One of the most heralded and promising peacetime applications of nuclear energy, a scheme to explode small atomic bombs deep in the earth to release natural gas trapped in subterranean rock formations, seems to have failed its early tests. Several experiments were conducted, the last in 1973, in an operation named Rio Blanco in western Colorado.

The nuclear explosions were intended to crack open the gas-bearing sandstone and create a large cavern into which the escaping gas could seep. But during test drilling at the site after the experiment, scientists made an embarrassing discovery. The blasts had apparently created three separate gas-filled caverns instead of one large one. The amount of gas recovered by drilling into the uppermost cavern was disappointingly small; it was estimated that it would cost an extra $1.5 million to reach the remainder of the released gas by drilling through to the other two caverns. In March, the Atomic Energy Commission announced that it was helping finance tests of another recovery technique that uses high-pressure fluids instead of nuclear explosions to crack gas-bearing sandstone.

BURNING WATER IN AN OIL FURNACE

At the height of the energy crisis in February, a British-born inventor announced the development of a process that could bring great savings in heating oil—without any reduction in energy output. Eric Cottell's recipe was simple: Merely add water. A blend of three parts oil and one part water, he claimed, would cut fuel consumption in an oil-fired heating system by at least a fifth.

Cottell's system emulsifies both fluids in an ultrasonic reactor—a refinement of a device he patented in 1952—which uses inaudible sound waves to break up liquid particles. It is used commercially to mix the ingredients for Worcestershire sauce, ketchup, cosmetics and paints. In an oil burner, a water-oil emulsion is fed into the flame; the water droplets explode into steam, shattering the surrounding layer of oil and exposing its maximum surface area. This provides more efficient and complete combustion.

Cottell tested the process in his home furnace and says it reduced fuel consumption by 25 per cent. Used over the winter in the heating plant of Long Island's Adelphi University, it saved more than 3,500 gallons of oil a week—about a 25 per cent reduction—and cut down the soot output by 98 per cent. Cottell announced plans to produce ultrasonic reactor units for home oil burners that would be no larger than a flashlight and cost between $100 and $150.

ENVIRONMENT

Two common substances, used by millions of people, were found to be extremely dangerous, even toxic; DDT, taken off the U.S. market as harmful in 1972, was again used to control pests; and a report on the use of herbicides in Vietnam showed the long-range effects these plant killers may have. Scientists also discovered that efforts to clean the air may backfire, and that the earth's ozone layer could be depleted by household products. Finally, a way was found to monitor water pollution with fish.

POISONOUS PRODUCTS

Asbestos and vinyl chloride, two substances that are used to make some of the most common products—upholstery, plastics, floor tiles, phonograph records, insulation—have been found to be insidiously dangerous. Exposure to even minute quantities of either over periods of time can cause a variety of deadly ailments, including cancer.

Researchers at Mount Sinai Medical Center in New York spent 20 years studying 933 workers who produced asbestos insulation at a Paterson, New Jersey, plant from 1941 to 1954. After discovering that 186 of the men had developed a form of lung cancer, the scientists in 1973 began X-ray examinations of some of the workers' families. They found that nearly 40 per cent of the 210 families tested had lung abnormalities common to asbestos workers. Four people who had come into contact with asbestos workers when they were children developed mesothelioma, a rare and invariably fatal form of cancer that is caused by exposure to asbestos fibers. Scientists fear that, because the asbestos industry is now 10 times larger than it was in the 1940s and 1950s, when the current illnesses developed, a plague of mesothelioma might break out sometime around the year 2000.

Equally as dangerous as asbestos is a colorless gas called vinyl chloride. The substance is used in everything from spray-can propellant to polyvinyl chloride, the ubiquitous plastic in hundreds of products from fountain pens to credit cards. In the United States alone, some 6,500 workers are regularly exposed to vinyl chloride and two million others work in industries that fabricate products from polyvinyl chloride.

The hazard first created a stir in January when the B.F. Goodrich Company reported that three workers in its Louisville vinyl-chloride conversion plant had died of angiosarcoma, an extremely rare form of liver cancer believed to be caused by inhalation of vinyl chloride.

The worst was yet to come; over the next few months, another 14 cases of angiosarcoma—all but two of them fatal —were reported among people who had worked with vinyl chloride in the United States. In June, a search of Connecticut health records disclosed that angiosarcoma had claimed the lives of two men who worked in the polyvinyl-chloride fabricating industry. That raised the possibility that hundreds of thousands of additional workers might have been exposed to the danger of liver cancer. It also appeared that vinyl chloride might cause birth defects and genetic damage and a wide range of cancers.

The U.S. Food and Drug Administration and the Environmental Protection Agency halted the distribution of spray products using vinyl chloride. In October, the Labor Department ordered a sharp reduction in workers' exposure to the substance, brushing aside industry protests that such strictures might cost 2.2 million jobs.

PLANT-KILLERS: A WAR WEAPON

After three years of investigation, the 17-member National Academy of Science's Committee on the Effects of Herbicides in Vietnam released its report in February. Its major conclusions: The military use of herbicides may have had ill effects on the human population of South Vietnam and inflicted long-term damage on the country's environment and supplies of timber.

In assessing the medical effects, the committee reported "no conclusive evidence of an association between herbicides and human birth defects." Like earlier investigations, however, it noted that following exposure of inhabitants to herbicides there were reports of coughing, vomiting, skin sores, dizziness and sometimes death.

The findings on vegetation were considerably more definite. Coastal mangrove forests "suffered greater damage than any other type of vegetation." Even where they were sprayed only once, they were destroyed. Time for total recovery of the forests: "at least 100 years."

The effects on cropland were less permanent. After a crop had been sprayed, only one growing season was lost; the toxic effect of residues barely persists beyond one year and does not have a "lasting detrimental effect" on plant nutrients in the soil.

BACK TO DDT?

After reviewing studies that indicated the widely used pesticides aldrin and dieldrin caused cancer in mice, the Environmental Protection Agency in October 1974 banned the production of the substances in order to avoid "unreasonable human health risks." It was the latest of increasingly rigid limitations on chemical defenses against insects. But the insects were already buzzing to the attack. Some pests that had been controlled by massive sprayings of pesticides had erupted in alarming numbers. The tussock moth is one. Millions of tussock moth larvae infested 650,000 acres of woodland in Washington state, Oregon and Idaho, where they began munching the needles off trees, causing them to wither and die. The possibility that a good deal of Pacific Coast timber would be destroyed led the government to relax the 1972 ban on DDT in January. By August 1974 the tussock was in check.

ACID BACKLASH FROM CLEANED AIR

Black smoke pouring from chimneys and smokestacks was not long ago a proud symbol of a community's industrialization and wealth. During the past few decades, however, drives for clean air and the recent environmental movement have·made smoke-scarred skies rare in most major cities of the United States and Western Europe. This achievement, paradoxically, has contributed to a new and growing environmental threat: acid rain. That was the conclusion of a report published in June by two environmental scientists, Gene E. Likens of Cornell and F. Herbert Bormann of Yale.

The two reported that the rain falling in the Eastern United States and in Eu-

rope has increased in acidity from 100 to 1,000 times normal levels within the last two decades. The chief villain in the increase has been sulfur dioxide, which combines with water to form sulfuric acid. Although the enforced burning of low-sulfur fuels, particularly natural gas, reduced the sulfur-dioxide output in major cities in the United States by 50 per cent during the 1960s, growing industrialization in suburban and rural areas has increased the net output of sulfur dioxide in the United States as a whole by 45 per cent. Furthermore, the requirement that plants build taller smokestacks to help disperse the pollutants over larger areas has, according to the report, "transformed local soot problems into a regional acid rain problem."

But the increase in—and the wider dispersion of—sulfur dioxide could not alone account for the dramatic rises in the acidity of rainfall. The answer, Likens and Bormann said, is a decrease in soot, stemming partly from a change from coal to such "clean" fuels as natural gas, and partly to the use of particle catchers, called precipitators, in smokestacks. The soot particles, they explained, are chemically alkaline. The great quantities of soot that were once released into the air along with sulfur dioxide tended to combine with the gas and neutralize it. Now that the soot is no longer there, animals, vegetation and man-made structures are feeling the full impact of an atmosphere laden with sulfur dioxide. There are, for example, indications that acid rain has already stunted the growth of forests in New England and Scandinavia, caused fish kills in Canadian lakes and corroded stone buildings—and there is even some evidence that it could have damaging effects on man himself.

EARTH'S OZONE SHIELD ATTACKED

Environmentalists have long been concerned about air pollution, but they have become aware only in the last year or so that man can inadvertently—and quickly—damage or even destroy a vital part of the atmosphere: the ozone layer. This layer of a special form of oxygen, some 15 to 30 miles above the earth, prevents

much of the deadly ultraviolet radiation given off by the sun from reaching the earth; without it, most terrestrial life would be wiped out.

But ozone forms a very fragile shield because the ozone molecule readily reacts with other gases and turns into an ordinary oxygen molecule, which is far less effective in blocking ultraviolet rays.

Among the gases that have an affinity for ozone are nitric oxides, which are given off in large quantities in the exhaust of supersonic aircraft. In August, a group of M.I.T. scientists reported that a fleet of 500 large supersonic transports in regular service would, within 25 years, decrease the amount of ozone in the layer by 12 per cent. A depletion that great would at the very least cause an increase in skin cancer among humans and harm many other forms of life.

In a September speech, Fred Iklé of the government's Arms Control and Disarmament Agency warned that nuclear war would bring thermonuclear explosions releasing nitric oxides in quantities large enough to deplete or perhaps even destroy the ozone layer.

Later that month, Ralph Cicerone, a physicist at the University of Michigan, warned that the ozone layer was endangered even by the propellant gases used in aerosol-spray cans. Such gases are finding their way into the ozone layer, where ultraviolet radiation breaks them down, causing a reaction with ozone.

Cicerone estimated that even if the use of aerosols were halted immediately, the gases already in the atmosphere would cause a 10 per cent reduction of ozone in the layer by 1990.

COUGHING FISH

Environmentalists looking for ways to monitor water pollution are turning for help to creatures that have a vested interest in clean water—fish. French technicians began the trend in 1973; they checked the waters of the Oise River by observing one peculiar kind of fish behavior: trout that are swimming upstream reverse their direction upon encountering pollution (Nature/Science Annual 1974, page 176). In April, scientists of the Environmental Protection Agency announced the discovery of another potentially useful piscatorial reaction in the behavior of bluefish, sunfish, flathead minnows, trout and salmon.

The researchers found that the fish began to cough more frequently when concentrations of mercury and copper became great enough to interfere with growth and reproduction. Aquatic biologist Robert Drummond, who directed the study, suggested that monitoring devices could be installed in waters near industrial and waste-treatment plants to record fish coughing and sound an alarm if there were any sudden increase. Environmentalists would thus be warned that a plant in the vicinity was releasing a potentially harmful effluent into the water and would be able to act immediately to halt the discharge.

GEOLOGY

In a year that took them all over the globe, geologists concentrated on several long-standing puzzles. The missing piece of a continent that split apart millions of years ago was believed found near the Falkland Islands; the green turtle's annual marathon swim from Brazil to Ascension Island was explained; the mystery surrounding precariously balanced rocks was unraveled; and the oldest living things—bacteria from one million years ago—turned up still viable in Antarctic ice.

FOUND: A CONTINENT'S LOST PIECE

An international expedition has apparently found the missing piece of the continental jigsaw puzzle that shows how Africa and South America were joined in the supercontinent of Gondwanaland 150 million years ago. During the past decade, geologists established that the underwater plateaus extending into the Atlantic from the two continents form a near-perfect fit with each other. The one gap remaining in the picture was a deep indentation in the Mozambique plateau off Durban, South Africa, which had no corresponding continental projection in South America to curl around and fit into

it. Finally, in July, aboard the research ship *Glomar Challenger,* a team led by Ian Dalziel of Columbia University and Peter Barker of the University of Birmingham discovered a fingerlike extension of the Falkland plateau, extending eastward from the Falkland Islands off South

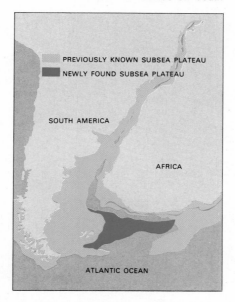

A NEW FIND: CONTINENTS WERE LINKED.

America. It was clear that the projection could reach around the Cape of Good Hope to fit the indentation on the Indian Ocean side of Africa.

To prove the extension was indeed the missing continental link and not a co-

incidental formation on the sea bottom, the geologists lowered a drill a mile and a half and bored through 1,835 feet of sediment to pull up core samples containing the material they were looking for: bedrock granite. Their find established that the rock below was part of the continental plateau and not ocean bottom, which normally is basaltic rock rather than granite.

WHY GREEN TURTLES SWIM SO FAR

One of the more prodigious feats of any of earth's living creatures is the long-distance swim made annually by the green turtle—from its grazing waters along the coast of Brazil to its nesting grounds on the beaches of Ascension Island, 1,200 miles away. Why the turtles swim so far to breed and how they find their tiny island target has long been a source of wonder to scientists. In May, an American and an Australian scientist provided a compelling answer: the instinct was bred into the amphibians by changes wrought over tens of millions of years as two continents drifted apart.

Zoologist Archie Carr of the University of Florida and paleontologist Patrick Coleman of the University of Western Australia suggest that the swim began as a short dip some 80 million years ago, after South America and Africa broke

A THEORY NOW EXPLAINS WHY BRAZILIAN TURTLES SWIM 1,200 MILES TO ASCENSION ISLAND.

apart and were separated by a gulf only several miles wide. Soon thereafter, lava welled up from the mid-gulf underwater ridge that marked the separation line of the continents, and the lava formed a volcanic island. The ancestors of the green turtle, which lived off the coast of what is now Brazil, soon found that the nearby island was a better nesting place than the mainland, where predators were constantly attacking their nests.

As the continents drifted farther apart, the island was eventually submerged. It was replaced by another island that had formed over the ridge, but the drift of South America had increased the distance from the mainland to the ridge and its island. Thus the turtles had to swim farther to find a nesting island. The process was repeated many times over millions of years, gradually increasing the length of the trip necessary to reach nesting islands. As a result, the turtles developed ever more powerful shoulder muscles and stores of heavy fat to provide energy on the long ocean journey.

But when the nesting islands finally got so far away that they could not be seen or scented from the South American coast, how did the turtles find them? By following the rising sun, Carr and Coleman think. They point out that the turtles now leave Brazil sometime between December and March for their eight-week trip to Ascension Island. During that period, the rising sun moves gradually northward and by swimming toward it, the turtles would follow a curving path that would take them close to the island. Significantly, the same path passes over a string of underwater mountains that in past eons may well have been the turtles' nesting islands.

SECRET OF THE BALANCED ROCKS

Balanced rocks—large boulders perched precariously atop a narrow stem of rock —have long puzzled laymen and scientists alike. They are formed when wind erodes a stratum of soft rock underlying a harder stratum; but how does the harder capstone stay balanced on the narrowing stem over centuries of erosion?

That question occurred to a Kansas State University engineer, Wilson Tripp,

after he photographed a Utah rock called the Goblet of Venus—a formation 13 feet tall with a frail-looking stem about 10 inches in diameter. Working with Fredric Appl, a Kansas State specialist in rock mechanics, Tripp finally hit upon the explanation reported in *Mechanical Engineering News* in February.

As the soft rock begins to erode, Tripp and Appl theorized, the harder capstone left above it begins to tilt. That movement shifts the capstone's center of gravity—and thus the greatest compressive force—to one side of the developing stem. The compressed side of the stem

erodes more slowly than the side under less pressure, resulting in an eventual reversal of the capstone's tilt toward the more heavily eroded side. The erosion rate then begins to increase on *that* side, and the tilting back and forth over the centuries finally results in a narrow stem supporting a large capstone. Eventually, when the stem becomes too narrow, the area of contact becomes too small for the self-leveling to continue and the capstone crashes to the ground. The theory was checked out by computer, but it failed to take into account a factor that had previously been the downfall of the

TOPPLED IN 1948, THIS FORMATION HELPED EXPLAIN AN UNUSUAL BALANCING ACT.

Goblet of Venus: two curious teenagers, who pushed against the Goblet and toppled it years before nature had a chance to take its course.

ONE MILLION YEARS OLD—AND ALIVE

Microbiologists Roy Cameron and Frank Morelli were drilling into Antarctica's icecap to check on surface contaminants that scientists' exploratory drills carried beneath the ice. What they found in their frozen soil samples were living bacteria that had apparently been buried in a state of suspended animation for as long as a million years. They recovered two types, both unlike any seen previously.

The bacteria from one sample, taken from Ross Island at a depth of 1,260 feet, were rod shaped; others, brought up from 280 feet below an area called New Harbor, were club shaped. When placed in nutrient broth, both species survived, but the club-shaped bacteria thrived and reproduced into a colony of doughnut-shaped organisms.

If the bacteria had been dormant but alive for a million years, the Antarctic discovery suggests that the exploration of Mars scheduled for 1976 may indeed find life there. Mars may perhaps have had favorable conditions for life—running water on its surface and a thick atmosphere—within the past million years, and perhaps its now dry and frigid soil harbors organisms waiting for moisture and heat to end their long sleep.

MEDICINE

Medical researchers compiled statistical reports revealing that deaths from nine major diseases declined sharply, and that the incidence of the common cold could be charted by age, educational level and income. Researchers also discovered that injections of meat tenderizer could cure backaches, and that an intrauterine contraceptive device was so dangerous that the manufacturer stopped all sales of the device. Several new techniques were exploited. One rendered milk, which is poisonous to some ethnic groups, safe to drink; another pro-

vided a better method for grafting skin; and a third showed how hearing impairments might be utilized to trace disorders in the brain.

THE KILLERS RISE AND FALL

Dramatic declines in 9 of the 15 leading causes of death among Americans—and frightening rises in three others—were reported in statistics released in May by the Department of Health, Education and Welfare. If the results were surprising *(The Death of Old Age, pages 106-121),* it was difficult to dispute their accuracy. The figures were based on a painstaking analysis of all 33,637,548 certificates of death that were recorded in the United States during the 1950s and 1960s.

Perhaps most remarkable was the 15 per cent drop in deaths over the past two decades from the leading killer: heart disease. The decline resulted from a trend that apparently began long before the current enthusiasm for exercise or dieting could have had any significant effect. The trend may have gone unnoticed, HEW experts explained, because previous studies did not adjust the death rates to compensate for the changing age profile in the United States; the average age is increasing, which means that unadjusted studies would unduly emphasize heart disease and other ailments of the aged.   has since proven

The largest decline discovered by the HEW study was in deaths from the major kidney diseases, nephritis and nephrosis; they declined 77 per cent, probably as a result of improved medical treatment. There was also a 28 per cent drop among men in deaths from peptic ulcers, a condition commonly associated with the stresses of business or professional life, but a slight increase of deaths among women. Other leading causes of death that showed a downward trend were arteriosclerosis, pneumonia and influenza, birth defects and accidents.

The sharpest increase in the death rate over the same two decades was in the category of chronic respiratory diseases —bronchitis, emphysema and asthma— which doubled during that period, suggesting that the nationwide concern over air pollution may be very well founded.

The danger of another belatedly recognized hazard to the health of Americans—alcoholism—is indicated by an alarming 67.1 per cent increase in deaths from cirrhosis of the liver.

The homicide rate, which was falling during most of the 1950s, leaped 75.5 per cent between 1958 and the end of 1969. But cancer, second only to heart attacks as a leading cause of death, showed a slow but steady rise of 3.4 per cent over 20 years.

WHO CATCHES COLD WHEN

The common cold may be common, afflicting all humans, but it strikes more frequently at some people than at others and, like its victims, seems more active on some days of the week than on others. That is the gist of a study published in January by two University of Michigan epidemiologists.

Arnold Monto and Betty Ullman based their report on the results of a six-year survey of 4,905 residents of Tecumseh, Michigan. Sorting out their subjects by age, the epidemiologists found that the greatest incidence of infection occurred among infants under the age of one—an average of 6.1 colds per year. The rate dropped steadily with increasing age (falling to only 1.3 per year for those older than 60) except for those between 20 and 29, who had a slightly higher infection rate than teenagers. The reason for the upswing in that group, the researchers suggested, is that people usually start their families during their twenties and thus are exposed to the frequent colds of their children.

Other findings:

● Among children under three, boys had more colds than girls. But beyond that tender age, females had colds more frequently than males.

● More colds seemed to start on Monday than on any other day of the week. Noting that the pattern is most pronounced in the school-age group, the researchers theorized that children are usually infected by others at the beginning of a school week and have developed a mature case of the sniffles by the succeeding Monday.

● The higher the income, the lower the

frequency of colds. That is understandable, said the epidemiologists, because poorer people generally live in more crowded conditions, increasing the prospects of infection.

• The incidence of colds was also greater among those with better education. For that surprising conclusion, the researchers could offer only the lame explanation that better-educated subjects more easily recognized minor symptoms as signs of illness.

DANGER FROM A CONTRACEPTIVE

One intrauterine device, or IUD, used as a contraceptive was taken off the market at the request of the U.S. Food and Drug Administration in June, and the effectiveness of others was questioned. The devices, long a subject of debate among doctors, are loops, coils and various other shapes set into a woman's uterus to prevent implantation of a fertilized egg —and thus prevent pregnancy. But the rate of pregnancy among the nearly five million women in the United States fitted with the IUD has been higher than among those using contraceptive pills and has run as high as 10 per cent with one device, the Dalkon shield. Furthermore, the IUD causes bleeding in some women and is rejected by the uterus in others.

In May, the manufacturer of the Dalkon shield warned that patients who became pregnant ran the risk of infection, miscarriage and even death, and a month later, sale of this device was stopped. In August, the FDA released statistics that seemed to justify its tough stand: since 1971, this IUD has caused severe infections that killed 11 women and led to abortions in 209 others.

TENDERIZING A BACKACHE

Meat tenderizer brings fast, fast relief for nagging backache, according to James Huddleston and Robert Boyd of Massachusetts General Hospital. They inject it into the spinal discs, the cushion-like pads that separate the vertebrae, the linked bones of the spinal column. Backache often arises when tissues surround-

ing the disc tear—usually as a result of physical strain; the disc then slips out of its normal position and pushes against the nerves in the spinal column, causing severe pain in the back and often extending into the legs as well.

Until now, physicians have usually prescribed bed rest and painkillers for victims of slipped discs—but sometimes they must remove the offending disc altogether and fuse the vertebrae that it separated. The new treatment requires no surgery. First the patient is given a general anesthetic, and a six-inch needle is jabbed into his spinal column. Then X-rays are taken. If they confirm that the point of the needle has penetrated into the tough cartilaginous fibers of the disc, chymopapain, the enzyme that is the active ingredient in meat tenderizers, is injected. The enzyme shrinks the spinal disc back into place, relieving pressure and the pain that it caused.

Huddleston and Boyd reported that they had achieved success in three quarters of the 300 experimental cases they treated over a three-year period. But other doctors have warned that the treatment (which has not yet been approved by the Food and Drug Administration for widespread use) may cause severe allergic reactions—and even blood-vessel and nerve damage.

MILK ANYONE CAN DRINK

One of the great frustrations of the post-World War II programs for donating American food to needy people elsewhere was the wholesale rejection of gifts of milk, a valuable source of scarce protein, particularly in Asia, Africa and Latin America. The recipients charged the milk was poison, and either threw it away or used it to paint their houses. Only later was it realized that, to these people, milk is indeed poison. It turned out that from 70 to 90 per cent of all adult non-Caucasians are unable to digest the sugar, lactose, in cow's milk. It can cause severe diarrhea and other intestinal disorders.

Removing the guilty lactose proved both expensive and impractical, since the lactose furnishes most of milk's caloric value. In May, two University of

Rhode Island scientists announced that they had developed a more satisfactory scheme. Instead of removing the lactose, they succeeded in converting it to glucose and galactose, two forms of sugar that most people can digest. Arthur Rand and James Hourigan found that the addition of the enzyme lactase changed whole milk into a low-lactose liquid up to four times as sweet—without reducing the caloric or nutritive values of milk. Equally important, lactase is inexpensive and can be added to milk at the same time it is pasteurized, at a cost of less than a penny a quart, thus making the modified milk an economical source of protein for millions of people around the world to whom milk—until now—has meant only misery.

GROWING SKIN FOR BURN GRAFTS

The ordeal—and the death rate—of seriously burned patients may soon be sharply reduced by a new technique for growing enough of a patient's skin in the laboratory to provide surgeons with an ample supply for covering his burns in a few operations. Until now, grafts have had to be surgically removed from the body of the burned patient one at a time in a lengthy series of operations.

The new method was found by Howard Igel and Aaron Freeman of the Akron Children's Hospital while they were looking for ways to grow tissue for cancer research. They discovered that human skin would grow and flourish on a patch of pigskin, which is commonly used as a dressing for burns.

Taking one square inch of healthy skin from a burn victim, they minced it with scissors and placed the fragments on the inner surface of the pigskin. After two weeks of incubation, as much as 50 square inches of human skin had grown on the pigskin. The doctors then grafted this new skin onto the patient, leaving the pigskin attached as a dressing. After two weeks, the pigskin had dried and begun to slough off, leaving the new skin, genetically identical to the patient's and thus almost certain to "take."

This laboratory-grown skin will not grow hair and has no sweat glands, but it is smooth and looks more normal than many conventional skin grafts. And because less skin has to be removed from the patient for grafting, he emerges less disfigured from the surgery.

TRACING BRAIN ILLS WITH SOUND

One of the serious side effects of brain disorders is impaired hearing. That fact was put to work by three researchers from the University of California at Irvine, who developed a way to make use of hearing impediments to locate disorders in the brain.

The procedure is begun by placing electrodes on the patient's scalp and earlobes. A series of loud clicks is then sent in rapid succession through earphones worn by the patient. As the nerve impulse generated in the inner ear by each click travels through the brain circuitry, it is detected by a supersensitive tracking system, isolated from other activity in the brain by a computer, and recorded. The result is a graph whose peaks represent the activity level at seven critical relay points along the auditory route. If there is brain damage near a relay point, that peak will be missing. (In a person of normal hearing there would be no missing peaks, therefore no way of tracing the brain disorder.)

The system has several advantages over other methods of diagnosis: it does not require the patient to describe what he hears—or even to be conscious. But most important, says Arnold Starr, Irvine's chief of neurology and one of the developers of the technique, "for the first time we can get information from the depth of the brain, and with a procedure that takes about four minutes."

PHYSICS

Einstein's theory that nothing can exceed the speed of light was joggled, though hardly overturned, by evidence suggesting that a theoretical faster-than-light particle called a tachyon might actually exist. Another Einsteinian theory—that the force of gravity never varies—came under attack, and according to one researcher was found wanting. Closer to home, detailed plans were outlined for gigantic space colonies that could be orbited between the earth and the moon. And Soviet and U.S. scientists got into another scholarly row over who was first to manufacture a brand-new element.

FASTER THAN THE SPEED OF LIGHT

Two Australian researchers have reported some puzzling phenomena that may well signal the existence of things that —contrary to the accepted laws of modern physics—travel faster than the speed of light. If such a phenomenon exists, it would be a particle, called a tachyon, that can travel *only* faster than the speed of light. It would need some bizarre properties. Its mass at rest would have to be an imaginary quantity; thus it would have to be always in motion. Unlike ordinary particles, which must gain energy to increase their speed, the tachyon would have its greatest energy near the speed of light and would thereafter lose energy as it accelerated to even higher velocities.

Roger Clay and Philip Crouch of the University of Adelaide decided that tachyons might be produced when cosmic rays (high-velocity particles from outer space) hit the atmosphere, shattering atoms of nitrogen and oxygen into a host of subatomic fragments. These particles, traveling near the speed of light, shower the earth a fraction of a second later. To spot any tachyons that might be produced, the Australians set up sensitive detectors that would be able to record the cosmic-ray showers and any particles that might precede them.

If tachyons indeed resulted from these collisions and did travel faster than the speed of light, the physicists reasoned, they would arrive at the earth earlier than did the other atomic fragments. Studying recordings of more than 1,300 cosmic-ray showers picked up by their detector early in 1973, the physicists found that 1,176 of them had been preceded (by about 60 millionths of a second) by the arrival of other particles. They decided that the early arrivals were not random events, but distinct phenomena. "Being unable to explain this result in a more conventional manner," the two scientists concluded, "we suggest that this is the result of a particle traveling with an apparent velocity greater than light."

IS GRAVITY WEAKENING?

There have been many challenges to Einstein's Theory of General Relativity since its presentation in 1916—all of them unsuccessful. But that record did not daunt Thomas Van Flandern of the U.S. Naval Observatory, who found evidence of what he believes is the gradual weakening of gravity, a force that according to general relativity never varies.

Van Flandern's evidence is based on the motion of celestial objects, which would be affected by a change in gravitational force. By studying the precise times that the moon has blocked from view various stars over the past 19 years, he calculated the changes in the moon's orbital velocity. The rate, he said, was twice the amount of slowdown that would be expected from known causes, principally the mutual tugs of tides on the earth and moon. The difference could be accounted for by a decrease in gravity of one part in 10 billion per year.

A discrepancy in the changes in the earth's rotation, also caused by the tidal effects, could similarly be explained by a decrease in gravitational force, according to Van Flandern. The same gradual phenomenon may even account for a gradual increase in the size of the earth, and thus explain such geological phenomena as sea-floor spreading and the movements of crustal plates.

WHERE TO PUT SPACE COLONIES

A practical use has finally been found for a discovery of the 18th Century mathematician Joseph Louis Lagrange: five constantly moving "libration" points in space where the gravitational and centrifugal forces of the earth-moon system cancel each other out. Any object placed at one of these points would remain there, falling neither toward the earth nor the moon. In May, Princeton physicist Gerard O'Neill proposed Lagrange's libration points as locations for permanent space colonies. O'Neill envisioned space communities enclosed in cylinders 16 miles long and four miles in diameter.

Each cylinder would contain air, water, farmland, fish, birds and other fauna, and could eventually support as many as 10 million humans. The cylinders would rotate to produce a centrifugal effect that would simulate gravity, enabling the occupants to live, work and play more or less normally on the cylinders' inner surfaces. Fixed mirrors focusing sunlight for steam generators would supply the electric power, and movable mirrors outside would reflect sunlight through windows at appropriate times and angles to create the effect of day and night—and even changing seasons.

A single, smaller colony—two cylinders 3,300 feet long and 650 feet in diameter—could be built in 15 to 20 years, said O'Neill. But even this bargain basement effort would cost roughly $25 billion —the total spent on the Apollo moon-landing program—and would require the transport of 10,000 tons of material from the earth. However, said O'Neill, the benefits of a colony in space would offset the cost. Most "dirty" industries on earth, he suggested, could be shifted to space and operated with nonpolluting technology by the middle of the next century. One day large portions of the human population would live in such colonies, turning the earth, in O'Neill's words, into "a worldwide park, a beautiful place for the colonists to visit for a vacation."

CLASH OVER ELEMENT 106

It became evident in September that the detente reached by the United States and the Soviet Union did not extend to their leading high-energy physics laboratories. For the third time in 10 years, the University of California's Lawrence Berkeley Laboratory and Russia's Joint Institute for Nuclear Research at Dubna disputed which had been the first to manufacture the newest man-made element.

A Berkeley team led by Albert Ghiorso and Nobel Laureate Glen Seaborg announced that they had succeeded in synthesizing element No. 106, a highly unstable substance composed of atoms that contained 106 protons each. Three

months earlier, when the Dubna group claimed to have produced the same element, Ghiorso characterized the Russians' proof of their achievement as "marginal" and insisted that the Soviet scientists were on "shaky ground." Similar disagreements had previously flared in 1964, when both laboratories claimed to have produced element No. 104, and in 1970, when the creation of element No. 105 was at issue.

To produce No. 106, the Berkeley group used a particle accelerator to fire oxygen atoms at a target composed of another man-made element: californium (No. 98). Sophisticated instruments indicated that some of the oxygen and californium had fused to form minute amounts of 106. The new element had a half-life of only nine tenths of a second: that is, half of its atoms disintegrated into simpler atoms in that brief time. At Dubna, the Russian group had claimed to have propelled chromium into a lead target to produce a different variety of No. 106; it had a half-life of less than a hundredth of a second.

Both sides agreed to hold off naming the new element until the issue of who produced it first is determined by the International Union of Pure and Applied Chemistry. That decision may be some time in coming. The union still has not ruled on who first synthesized elements Nos. 104 and 105.

TECHNOLOGY

A recently discovered notebook by Leonardo da Vinci revealed that the master engineer had invented some present-day devices not reinvented until recent times. Meanwhile, technology provided a new technique to help the blind see, a machine that allows its user to feel objects that do not exist, extra-large TV screens, and a proposal to use molecules as electronic components. In the Soviet Union, scientists tested the world's largest and most unusual aircraft.

LEONARDO, MAGNIFICENT INVENTOR

With the publication in September of the Madrid Codices (found in Madrid's National Library in 1965), the full extent of Leonardo da Vinci's genius as a mechanical engineer was established. Few of Leonardo's inventions were ever actually built, but he did not hold back his artistic talents in drawing them, and the Codices add to the extensive list of modern machines he devised—several centuries too soon.

Although the invention of the bicycle has been set at 1839 and ascribed to a Scotsman named Kirkpatrick Macmillan, Leonardo devised a chain-driven, two-

LEONARDO'S CHAIN-DRIVE BIKE RESEMBLES THE MODERN VERSION.

wheeled vehicle at the end of the 15th Century. In the 1920s engineers at the Sperry Gyroscope Company came up with what they thought was an ingenious design for a bearing to stabilize a rapidly spinning aircraft gyro. Just such a bearing assembly—drawn in meticulous detail—appears in the Codices. The invention of a worm gear, now used in automobile steering linkages, was credited to 18th Century clockmaker Henry Hindley; it too appears in the Codices.

Perhaps the only major invention by Leonardo not "discovered" later by others was his scheme for casting extralarge bronzes. Around 1500 he designed an equestrian statue of the Milanese duke Francesco Sforza to be the largest bronze of its time. Some 23 feet high and weighing 158,000 pounds, it was to be cast upside down in the ground in such a way that the mold would not crack. The project was not finished, however, as invading French soldiers shot the mold to pieces with their crossbows.

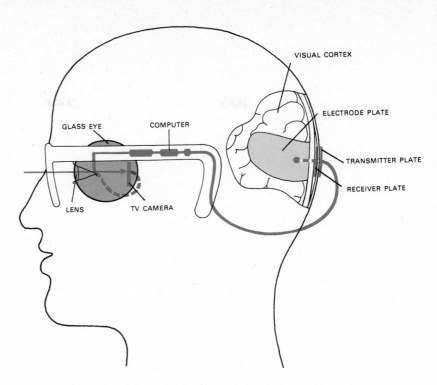

A GLASS EYE WITH A TV CAMERA MAY HELP THE BLIND "SEE."

A TV EYE FOR THE BLIND

To provide eyes for the blind has long been the dream of scientists. In February, that dream moved closer to fruition as American and Canadian researchers announced a breakthrough in producing artificial sight in the blind.

Biophysicist William Dobelle and computer expert Michael Mladejovsky, both of the University of Utah, and neurosurgeon John Girvin of the University of Western Ontario worked with two blind patients, one 29 and the other 43 years old. During operations performed with local anesthetics, a grid of 64 electrodes was placed in contact with the visual center on the right half of the cortex of each patient's brain. Then, while individual electrodes were activated by tiny pulses of electricity, the patients described where they "saw" phosphenes —the stars, flickers and sometimes even elaborate patterns of light that people sometimes perceive when their eyes are closed. Some were "higher," some "to the right," while others were "lower."

The scientists were able to control the pattern of phosphenes by watching a computer-operated screen that displayed

the patients' responses, and showed approximately where in the field of "vision" each electrode produced a phosphene. These patterns were perceived by one of the patients who was able to draw squares, triangles and letters of the alphabet corresponding to the designs generated by the electrodes.

Dobelle was encouraged enough to predict the development of a system that would give the blind a certain amount of artificial vision. It would consist of a tiny television camera embedded in the glass eye of a blind person and connected to a miniaturized computer in the frames of the eyeglass. All of the new, small-scale technology would be wired to electrodes placed permanently in the brain. "The blind person would not have normal vision," Dobelle cautioned, "but it would be good enough for him to get around chairs and tables, make out doorways and buildings and eventually read, at a slow but useful speed."

AN ADDED MOVIE FEATURE: FEELIES

Although many things predicted by Aldous Huxley in his novel *Brave New*

World—published in 1932—have come true, one that has not is "Feelies": movies that enable each member of the audience, by grasping a metal globe, to feel the tactile sensations being experienced by actors on the screen. Now, the Feelies may be just a tingle away. In February, the Polytechnic Institute of New York reported that computer engineer Michael Noll had built a "tactile simulation device" that almost achieves the effect Huxley imagined.

Noll's machine, designed and constructed as part of his work for his Ph.D., consists of a large box with a protruding stalk topped with a knob about the size of a billiard ball. When the device is turned on, anyone moving the knob gets the impression that it is encountering an object—even though there really is nothing there. In fact, the "object," such as a sphere or cube, or even an elephant, exists only in the form of equations describing its surface. These equations are programed into a computer that controls three electric motors within the box. The computer continuously calculates the position of the knob and applies power to the motors so that a person moving the knob can "feel" it sliding along or bouncing off the simulated surface.

MOLECULAR ELECTRONICS

The remarkable feats of electronic miniaturization that create pocket-sized calculators with microscopically etched circuits no larger than a postage stamp may be overshadowed in the future by a concept announced in March by two chemists. They proposed making use of tailor-made, individual molecules as electronic components.

Arieh Aviram of IBM and Mark Ratner of New York University explained that their idea was based on a familiar property of the molecule: The higher the "binding energy" that holds it together, the less likely it is to lose electrons—the particles making up electric currents. By combining two or more small molecules with large enough differences in their binding energies, they could theoretically produce a large molecule that could form an electronic component.

Such a molecule, for example, could be used as a rectifier—a device that allows a flow of current through it in only one direction and that is widely used to convert alternating current (AC) into direct current (DC). One end of this molecular rectifier would consist of a molecule with a relatively low binding energy, making it a donor of electrons. On the other end of the rectifier would be a molecule with a high binding energy; it would act as an electron acceptor. If an external, alternating current were applied to the device, electrons would flow only in one direction: from the donor to the acceptor.

Aviram and Ratner admitted that the construction of such a molecular rectifier could be complicated by the fact that the donor and acceptor sites might not be localized at either end of the molecule. That might produce an unwanted interaction between the sites—the molecular version of a short circuit. But by using organic (carbon-based) molecules, which can be created in an enormous variety of structures, chemists could fashion an insulating bridge between the donor and acceptor sites, thus preventing short circuits.

If they were able to demonstrate the concept experimentally, the researchers predicted, it might open the way for an era of "organic electronics," in which

A SOVIET PLANE, THE WORLD'S LARGEST, PRODUCES A BUBBLE OF AIR TO KEEP IT AFLOAT.

chemical laboratories would begin to turn out electronic devices with as much ease as they are able to manufacture synthetic fabrics today.

A MONSTER FLYING ON A BUBBLE

Western intelligence sources who first reported the strange creation in January called it the Caspian Sea Monster. It was a fitting name. The 10-engine flying boat that the Soviets were testing over the Caspian Sea was the world's largest aircraft—an estimated 500 tons (versus less than 400 tons for the largest U.S. plane, the C-5 Galaxy)—and the most unusual. For it operates by a deliberate combination of aerodynamic lift and "ground effect," the air-cushion phenomenon that lifts a Hovercraft. (Other big airplanes —notably the German 12-engine Dornier Do-X of 1929—have taken advantage of ground effect to get aloft, but in most cases unintentionally because the effect was little understood then.)

On takeoff, the jet blast from eight engines mounted on a stubby, 40-foot-long forward wing is deflected down at an angle against the water, creating a bubble that produces extra lift under the 125-foot main wing toward the rear. This force and the conventional lift provided by the main wing when two tail-mounted engines thrust the airplane forward are enough to pull the giant off the water. When sufficient forward speed has been

gained, the blast from the eight jets can be redirected over the top of the main wings, providing additional thrust.

The monster can skim as low as 25 to 50 feet above the water—making it difficult to detect by radar—at airspeeds ranging from 100 to about 350 miles per hour, and it can operate without refueling for as long as two to three days over ranges as great as 7,000 miles. Its long range and low altitude plus its capacity to carry a 15- to 20-man crew and tons of electronic equipment suggest that it was designed to hunt submarines.

MOVIE-SIZED COLOR TV

Color-television pictures as big as home movies became available—for a price —when two companies resurrected the 1930s idea of using a lens to project onto a screen the image from a small video tube rather than showing the image directly on a big tube.

Both Sony, the Japanese electronics giant, and Advent Corporation, a hi-fi component maker of Cambridge, Massachusetts, offered units providing pictures as large as four by six feet. They are projected onto space-age aluminized screens (the surface of Sony's is only 30 microns, or .00012 inch, thick) that are several times more reflective than ordinary movie screens, giving a brighter, sharper picture. Advent uses three picture tubes in its projector; each tube produces an image in red, blue or green —the primary colors of all color TV transmission. Sony employs a single, powerful tube to make the three colors. The high cost for such gadgetry: $3,000 for the Sony, $2,500 for the Advent.

ZOOLOGY

The bizarre ability of some lizards to run on water was finally explained. And on land, conservationists suffered a setback in their battle to save wild mustangs when the government, citing overcrowding on the range, launched a roundup of the wild horses.

WALKING ON WATER—HOW IS IT DONE?

THE LIZARD THAT RUNS ON WATER

How the basilisk lizard of Mexico and Central America manages to run on water was explained by Joshua Laerm of the University of Illinois. Analyzing slow-motion films, he discovered that the lizard runs on its hind legs and keeps most of its body above the surface. It waddles rapidly in a way that allows it to push itself ahead with maximum force. At the same time, it retracts each leg from the water for the next step with a minimum of resistance.

Laerm concluded that two factors enable the basilisk to keep its body safely above the water: the speed with which it retracts its feet from the water and the large surface area of its feet.

WRANGLE OVER WILD MUSTANGS

A conservationist movement led by Velma "Wildhorse Annie" Johnston seemed to have saved the wild mustangs, descendants of the proud Spanish horses brought to the New World in the 15th Century, from extermination by hunters for pet-food processors. But by 1974 the mustang population had grown to nearly 43,000 and was increasing 20 per cent a year; the government ordered a roundup.

Wild mustangs were corraled by wranglers in Oregon. And no one is certain what will happen to them. While captured animals are supposed to be distributed to private citizens willing to care for them, there is no clause in the federal law for supervision to prevent the horses from being abused or slaughtered for pet food. If the law is not strengthened, conservationists claim, the once-numerous species will vanish altogether.

WILD MUSTANGS, AT REPOSE HERE IN THE MOUNTAINS, ARE THREATENED BY ROUNDUPS.

Nobel Prize Winners

ALBERT CLAUDE

GEORGE EMIL PALADE

CHRISTIAN RENÉ DE DUVE

In 1974, Nobel prizes in the sciences went to researchers who explored some of the smallest and largest bodies recognized by science. The awards in medicine and chemistry acknowledged breakthroughs in the study of human cell structures, and in the long-chain molecules called polymers that are used to make plastics. A bold new technique that can observe massive and distant stellar bodies earned astronomers the physics award—the first presented to researchers in radio astronomy.

CHEMISTRY

"It's 6 a.m. and I'm not yet awake," grumbled Stanford University chemist Paul Flory when a British journalist called him to inquire about his winning the Nobel prize in chemistry. Flory may have been sleepy then, but he had spent many wide-awake hours in the laboratory. Perhaps more than any other chemist, Flory made possible the modern world of plastics by showing chemists how to compare the characteristics of synthetic materials. Flory helped develop nylon, one of the first truly synthetic molecules, while he was employed by the Du Pont Company. But his later accomplishments were more basic, theoretical work that explained how molecules can change into substances with widely different physical properties.

Flory discovered that each of the various kinds of polymers—the very large, chainlike molecules that make up natural substances like protein as well as plastics—has an intermediate temperature at which its properties can be easily studied and then compared with other polymers. Flory also succeeded in describing mathematically how lengthy polymer chains become extended when heated above their "Flory temperatures."

This finding has allowed other chemists to make polymers to order by controlling the distance between their sections. Large distances can produce liquids like paints, intermediate distances make "soft" rubbers, and tightly packed chains can be made into "hard" plastics.

PHYSIOLOGY OR MEDICINE

For years the cells that make up the body were as mysterious as a distant planet. Now, perception of the cell has changed: instead of a vague component it is known to be a highly complex miniature world that, like the body of which it is a part, is equipped with specialized organs. Much of the new understanding of the cell is the result of pioneering work—spread over nearly 50 years —by three scientists whose accomplishments earned them the year's Nobel award for medicine. The winners were Albert Claude of the Free University of Brussels' Jules Bordet Institute, George Palade of Yale University's School of Medicine, and Christian de Duve of New York's Rockefeller University and the University of Louvain in Belgium. All three did most of their experimental work at Rockefeller University, which, in producing 15 laureates since 1901, has become a kind of Nobel prize factory.

Albert Claude, an American raised in Belgium, is truly the father of modern cell biology. From 1929 to 1949 Claude devoted most of his efforts to learning how cancer viruses invade and alter healthy cells. While he did not unravel the mystery of cancer, Claude was the first to view cancer-virus particles in tumor cells. His most significant contribution to biology, however, was the method, now standard, for examining the structure and chemistry of individual

PAUL JOHN FLORY

MARTIN RYLE

ANTONY HEWISH

cells. Called differential centrifugation, Claude's technique uses an extremely high-speed centrifuge—a machine like a cream separator—which sorts substances of different densities by spinning them rapidly, to study the parts of a living cell.

Born in Romania, George Palade expanded Claude's technique to isolate and describe the ribosome, a tiny granular component of the cell. He subsequently demonstrated that the ribosome functions as a kind of miniature factory, producing the protein that the cell needs to stay alive and healthy.

The third recipient of the prize, Christian de Duve, a Belgian citizen, discovered lysosomes, subcellular organisms that act as microscopic stomachs, digesting foreign material like bacteria that enter the cell.

PHYSICS

For the first time since it began awarding the Nobel prizes in 1901, the Swedish Academy of Sciences presented an award for achievements in radio astronomy. Sharing the $125,000 physics award were two British astronomers: Martin Ryle and Antony Hewish, both of whom did the work leading to their prizes at Cambridge University.

Over two decades, starting in 1952, Ryle developed and perfected a technique that revolutionized radio astronomy. Astronomers had been constructing ever-larger dish antennas in an attempt to detect radio emissions from objects millions of light-years away from earth where light cannot be picked up by optical telescopes. They knew, however, that more distant objects would require antennas several miles wide—making them extraordinarily difficult to construct.

Ryle's solution was disarmingly simple: he clustered several small radio telescopes together and thus achieved the observational power of the mammoth antennas astronomers

had said they could not build. With this new technique, radio astronomers have been able to scan numerous slices of sky simultaneously over long periods of time. By piecing signals from distant radio-wave-emitting objects into a mosaic, they have been able to infer far more about the size and structure of the universe than have astronomers using single-dish antennas. In fact, the long time-exposure of Ryle's telescopes allow "viewing" with a definition so sharp, that in the words of the Nobel selection committee, "it corresponds to an observer on earth being able to see the details of a postage stamp on the moon."

Hewish was also cited for his work with radio telescopes. But while most radio astronomers were using long-time-exposure methods, Hewish took quick "snapshots" of the sky—in hopes of finding short-lived stellar phenomena missed by his colleagues. The team he led at Cambridge succeeded brilliantly; they discovered pulsars, bizarre galactic objects that emit powerful radio waves at precise regular intervals. The first pulsar signals startled Hewish, who thought his team might have stumbled upon messages from an advanced galactic civilization. He gave the hush-hush project the half-joking code name L.G.M. (for Little Green Men), but soon discovered three more of the pulsating objects scattered widely across the Milky Way, an indication that they were natural phenomena.

Hewish postulated that the weird pulses were coming from stars that had collapsed, crushing them into small, incredibly dense, rapidly spinning spheres that spew out intense radio waves. These stars would appear to pulse as the area of most intense radiation on their surfaces faced the earth and then swung away, much as the light from a lighthouse flickers as it turns toward and away from the viewer.

Credits

Sources for the illustrations in this book are shown below.
Credits from left to right are separated by semicolons, from
top to bottom by dashes.

Cover—Jeff Simon. 6—NASA. 7—American Science & Engineering,
Inc. 8,9—High Altitude Observatory, National Center for Atmospheric
Research. 10,11—The Aerospace Corporation. 12,13—U.S. Naval Re-
search Laboratory. 15—Drawing by Nicholas Fasciano. 16—Charles
Lindsay. 17—From *The Vinland Map And The Tartar Relation*, by R. A.
Skelton, Thomas E. Marston and George D. Painter, published by Yale
University Press, © 1965 Yale University. 18,19—Map by Kathy Wid-
mer. 22,23—Painting by Jack Endewelt. 24,25—Department of Indian
and Northern Affairs, Parks Canada. 26,27—Birgitta Wallace, Carnegie
Museum. 31—Charles Lindsay. 32—M. Suhara. 33 through 39—© Cine-
Science, Japan, photographer Jun-ichiro Takeda, stills by Dan McCoy
from Black Star. Drawings by Nicholas Fasciano. 40—Dominick Maio.
42—Walter T. Silver. 43—Hope Ryden. 45—Dominick Maio—Ted Russell, from TIME-LIFE Picture Agency—Stan Wayman, from TIME-LIFE
Picture Agency. 46—Map by Melanie Schwartz. 48—Hampshire Col-
lege, courtesy Raymond Coppinger. 49—Jay Lorenz. 52,53—Jack
Swedberg. 54—Henry Groskinsky. 56—Henry Groskinsky—Kennecott
Copper Corporation. 58—Drawings by Nicholas Fasciano. 60—Flip
Schulke from Black Star; Summa Corp. 61—Drawings by Nicholas Fa-
sciano. 62,63—Map by Dick Abarno. 65—Drawing by Nicholas Fasci-
ano. 67—Fritz Goro, from TIME-LIFE Picture Agency. 68—Map by
Nicholas Fasciano. 69—John P. Milton. 70,71—Peter Jackson, World
Wildlife Fund; G. D. Plage from Bruce Coleman, Inc. 72—George Silk,
from TIME-LIFE Picture Agency. 73—Tiger Tops Jungle Lodge. 74,75
—George Silk, from TIME-LIFE Picture Agency. 76—Terence Spencer.
77—G. D. Plage from Bruce Coleman, Inc. 78—George Silk, from TIME-
LIFE Picture Agency. 79—George Silk, from TIME-LIFE Picture Agency
—John P. Milton. 80—George Silk, from TIME-LIFE Picture Agency
—G. D. Plage from Bruce Coleman, Inc. 81,82,83—George Silk, from
TIME-LIFE Picture Agency. 84—Fred Conrad. 86—Robert W. Kelley,
from TIME-LIFE Picture Agency—Ernie Hearion for *The New York
Times*. 88—Don Hogan Charles for *The New York Times*. 90,91—Barry
J. Naster, courtesy Behavior Research Laboratory, Anna State Hos-
pital, Anna, Illinois. 94,95—Allan Grant. 96—Brown Brothers. 97—NASA

courtesy Hughes Aircraft Company. 98—Hughes Aircraft Company. 99
—Hughes Aircraft Company, courtesy Western Union Corporation;
Hughes Aircraft Company. 100,101—Dennis Rice; NASA, courtesy Fair-
child Industries. 102,103—Fairchild Industries. 104—Drawing by Fred
Werner. 105—Western Union Corporation. 106—Hanna W. Schreiber
from Rapho-Guillumette. 109—Fritz Goro, from TIME-LIFE Picture
Agency, courtesy Harvey Wolinsky, Albert Einstein College of Med-
icine. 110—Tass from Sovfoto. 111—John Launois from Black Star. 112
—Al Freni. 114—Drawing by Nicholas Fasciano, courtesy Dr. Allan
Goldstein, University of Texas Medical Branch. 116—John Zimmerman
from FPG—Fritz Goro, from TIME-LIFE Picture Agency. 117—Fritz
Goro, from TIME-LIFE Picture Agency. 118—Al Freni. 123—William J.
Weber. 124—William Bolte. 125—Ron Willocks. 126—M. Timothy
O'Keefe—Jeff Simon. 127—Map by Nicholas Fasciano. 128—Jeff Si-
mon. 129—Robert E. Pelham from Bruce Coleman, Inc. 130—William
Partington Jr. except top left M. Timothy O'Keefe. 131—Jeff Simon.
132,133—Henry Groskinsky. 135—Thomas Eisner. 136—Alain Nogués
from Sygma. 138,139—Maps by Pamela Szopo Krent. 142—Wide World
—Jehangir Gazdar from Woodfin Camp and Associates. 143—Photo-
reporters, Inc. 144—Gianni Tortoli for F.A.O. 145—Marc and Evelyne
Bernheim for the Rockefeller Foundation, from Woodfin Camp and As-
sociates. 146—Françoise Viard from Gamma. 149—Brian Brake from
Rapho-Guillumette. 151—NASA. 152—NASA. 153—NASA—Charles Boy-
er. 154,155—NASA. 156—Frank Kiernan, Yerkes Regional Primate
Research Center of Emory University. 161—Flip Schulke from Black
Star—David K. Caldwell from Biological Systems, Inc. 163—Bob
Combs. 165—Nina Leen, from TIME-LIFE Picture Agency. 166—Melvin
Konner, from Anthro-Photo, Harvard University. 167—Spencer L. Rog-
ers, San Diego Museum of Man; UPI. 168—Drawing by Carolynne
Poon, courtesy Robson Bonnichsen and Larry Lahren; map by Wy-
oming Archaeological Society. 171—Stanford Research Institute. 177
—Map drawn for TIME by W. Hortens—Archie Carr, University of
Florida. 178—Wilson Tripp, Kansas State University. 182—By permis-
sion, from *The Unknown Leonardo*, © 1974 McGraw-Hill Book Co.
(U.K.) Ltd. 183—Drawing by Nicholas Fasciano, courtesy Bill Dobelle,
University of Utah. 184—Aviation Week & Space Technology. 185
—Ralph Morse, from TIME-LIFE Picture Agency; Bill Eppridge, from
TIME-LIFE Picture Agency. 186—Jiri Jiru—Yale University News Bu-
reau—Eugene H. Kone, Rockefeller University. 187—Stanford Univer-
sity News and Publication Service—Wide World Photos (2).

Acknowledgments

Portions of this book were written by Alan Anderson, Harry Atkins,
Lucy Burchard, Hal Field, Tom Froncek, Ben Haimowitz, Leon Jaroff
and Stephanie Wald. The editors of this book also wish to thank the following persons and institutions for their assistance: Nathan Azrin, Professor, Rehabilitation Institute Department, Southern Illinois University,
Carbondale; Andrew Benson, Professor of Biology, Scripps Institution
of Oceanography, Marine Biology Research Division, La Jolla, California; Awinash Bhatkar, Research Associate, Dept. of Entomology
and Nematology, University of Florida, Gainesville; Virginia H. Black,
Associate Professor of Cell Biology, New York University Medical
School, New York City; Warren W. Blandin, Chief of Wildlife Research,
Division of Fisheries and Game, Field Headquarters, Westboro, Massachusetts; David Bohlin, U.S. Naval Research Laboratory, Washington, D.C.; Robson Bonnichsen, Assistant Professor of Anthropology,
University of Maine, Orono; Reid A. Bryson, Professor of Meteorology
and Geography, Director of the Institute for Environmental Studies,

University of Wisconsin, Madison; David K. Caldwell, Associate Pro-
fessor of Speech, Head of the Biocommunication and Marine Mammal
Research Facility, University of Florida, St. Augustine; Melba C. Cald-
well, Research Instructor, Biocommunication and Marine Mammal
Research Facility, University of Florida, St. Augustine; Alex Comfort,
Center for the Study of Democratic Institutions, Santa Barbara, Cal-
ifornia; Walter Courtenay, Professor of Zoology, Florida Atlantic
University, Boca Raton; Ben Day, Biologist, Vermont Department of
Fish and Game, Montpelier; Dr. Albert Decker, Executive Director of
The New York Fertility Research Foundation, Inc., New York City; W.
Donner Denckla, Endocrinologist, Roche Institute of Molecular Biol-
ogy, Nutley, New Jersey; Henry DiCristina, Manager for Systems Tests,
Integration and Launch Operations for Westar, Hughes Aircraft Com-
pany, El Segundo, California; Ropert E. Dubos, Curator of Vertebrates,
University of Connecticut, Storrs; John Eddy, High Altitude Observa-
tory, Boulder, Colorado; Thomas Eisner, Professor of Biology, Cornell
University, Ithaca, New York; Robert L. Fleming, Kathmandu, Nepal;
Richard Foxx, Behavior Research Laboratory, Anna State Hospital,
Anna, Illinois; Walter Garey, Research Physiologist, Scripps Institution

of Oceanography, La Jolla, California; Robert Gerard, Coordinator, Inter-University Ferromanganese Program, Lamont-Doherty Geological Observatory, Palisades, New York; Allan Goldstein, Director, Division of Biochemistry, University of Texas Medical Branch, Galveston; Morris Greene, Assistant Director, Food and Agriculture Organization Liaison Office, United Nations; Carl Gustavson, Professor of Psychology, Eastern Washington State College, Cheney; Dr. Denham Harman, Professor of Biochemistry and Medicine, University of Nebraska College of Medicine, Omaha; Dr. Leonard Hayflick, Professor of Microbiology, Stanford University School of Medicine, Stanford, California; Barbara Horn, Geologist, Odessa, Texas; David R. Horn, Geologist, Odessa, Texas; Dr. Pascal James Imperato, First Deputy Health Commissioner, New York City; Allan R. Keith, New York City; Wayne King, Curator of Herpetology, New York Zoological Park, Bronx, New York; Fred D. Kochendorfer, Program Manager, Pioneer Program, NASA, Washington, D.C.; Joshua Laerm, Instructor of Zoology, University of Illinois, Urbana; Garvey Laurent, Food and Agriculture Organization, United Nations; Dr. Frederick Ludwig, Professor of Pathology and Radiological Sciences, California College of Medicine, University of California, Irvine; Charles Lindsay, Staff Archeologist, National Historic Parks and Sites Branch, Parks Canada, Ottawa; Peter Marler, Professor of Animal Behavior, Rockefeller University, New York City; Earl B. Mayfield, The Aerospace Corporation, Los Angeles, California; John L. Mero, President, Ocean Resources, Inc., La Jolla, California; Dr. Kalidas Nandy, Associate Professor of Anatomy, Emory University, Atlanta, Georgia; Brian O'Leary, Assistant Professor of Astronomy, Hampshire College, Amherst, Massachusetts; Voit B. Richens, Maine Cooperative Wildlife Research Unit, University of Maine, Orono; C. Richard Robins, Professor of Biology and Living Resources, Ro-

senstiel School of Marine and Atmospheric Sciences, University of Miami, Florida; Carl Robinson, Warden, Connecticut Correctional Institution, Somers; Peter A. Rona, Research Geophysicist, National Oceanic and Atmospheric Administration, Atlantic Oceanographic and Meteorological Laboratories, Miami, Florida; Charles L. Ross, High Altitude Observatory, Boulder, Colorado; David Ross, Department of Geology and Geophysics, Woods Hole Oceanographic Institution, Woods Hole, Massachusetts; Duane Rumbaugh, Professor of Psychology, Georgia State University, Atlanta; Hope Ryden, New York City; Albert Scheckenbach, Unit Manager, Medical Center for Federal Prisoners, Springfield, Missouri; Bengt Schonback, Keeper, Iron Age Department, Royal Academy of History and Antiquities, Stockholm, Sweden; C. W. Severinghaus, Wildlife Biologist, New York State Department of Environmental Conservation, Delmar; Ross Simons, Office of the Assistant Secretary for Science, Smithsonian Institution, Washington, D.C.; William Siapno, Chief Scientist, Deepsea Ventures, Gloucester Point, Virginia; Bernard Strehler, Professor of Biology, University of Southern California, Los Angeles; Giuseppe Vaiana, Center for Astrophysics, Cambridge, Massachusetts; David P. Visel, The Aerospace Corporation, Los Angeles, California; Birgitta L. Wallace, Research Assistant, Carnegie Museum, Pittsburgh, Pennsylvania; Willard Whitcomb, Professor of Entomology, University of Florida, Gainesville; Werner Wicke, Project Designer, L'Anse aux Meadows, National Historic Parks and Sites Service, Parks Canada, Ottawa; Joe Wiley, New Hampshire Fish and Game Department, Concord; Charles Willey, Biologist, Vermont Department of Fish and Game, Montpelier; George Withbroe, Center for Astrophysics, Cambridge, Massachusetts; Roger Wolfe, Mental Hygiene Unit, Connecticut Correctional Institution, Somers.

Index

Numerals in italics indicate an illustration of the subject mentioned.